UNIVERSITY COURSES
IN EDUCATION in the UK
open to students
from overseas

2003/2004

Published by
The Universities Council for the Education of Teachers
(Registered Charity No. 275082)

58 Gordon Square, London WC1H 0NT
T: 020 7580 8000
F: 020 7323 0577
E: ucet@ioe.ac.uk
W: www.ucet.ac.uk

CONTENTS

CONTENTS

This compendium describes initial, postgraduate and post-experience courses in education in British universities available to students from overseas. It includes entries from most universities and university-sector colleges in the United Kingdom.

The Compendium is compiled and published by the Universities Council for the Education of Teachers. The original UCET came into existence in 1967. In 1993 UCET and the Polytechnics Council for the Education of Teachers formed the enlarged Universities Council for the Education of Teachers, which was joined in 1997/98 by a number of university-sector Colleges of Higher Education, some of whom now bear the title *University College*. Since 2000 virtually all Scottish universities have joined the Council.

UCET acts as a national forum for the discussion of all matters relating to the education of teachers and to the study of education in universities. It makes a contribution to the formulation of policy in these fields and makes representations to and collaborates with other groups in the United Kingdom with similar interests. The Council has a number of standing committees, each with a special concern, as for instance in pre-service education and training - primary, secondary and post-16, continuing professional education and research. One committee has a special responsibility in the field of work with students from overseas and it was on its initiative that this compendium was originally prepared in 1982.

Members of UCET hope that the handbook will be of use to students, experienced teachers and others seeking educational qualifications in this country. Prospectuses and further information should be requested from the individual universities/colleges. Websites of most of the institutions can be accessed via the UCET website: www.ucet.ac.uk.

The entries in this compendium are compiled by the institutions concerned. The work of gathering, collating and editing the information for the current edition has been handled by Ruth Klassen, Publications Editor and Web Manager to UCET.

Mary J Russell
Secretary, UCET

May 2002

Teacher Education in the United Kingdom

The teaching profession in the UK has an all-graduate entry and it is necessary for new teachers to have professional training in education as well as a high standard of competence in the subjects they will teach before they can achieve 'qualified teacher status' (QTS) and be allowed to practise in State-run schools. There are a variety of ways of obtaining QTS, two of them being the main methods of qualifying in the university system:

- by taking a degree that combines the study of education with the subject or subjects to be taught (BEd, BA, BSc)
- by taking a specialist subject degree followed by a Postgraduate Certificate in Education (PGCE)*, normally of one year's duration.

The PGCE is designed specifically for graduates who are preparing to enter teaching; it concentrates on aspects of education closely related to school teaching and much of the course is spent in schools. All entrants to initial teacher training must have attained in Mathematics and English Language the standard required to achieve a grade C in the GCSE examination and, since September 1998, in Science (primary teachers only).

In addition to courses for the *initial* training of teachers, there are various opportunities for advanced study open to qualified teachers with several years' experience. Many of these courses include options and areas of study that are particularly relevant to the needs of teachers from overseas countries. Programmes for experienced teachers include one year full-time (or equivalent part-time) Diploma courses in a variety of fairly specialised fields relating for instance to age ranges, Special Education Needs or particular areas of the curriculum. Masters courses in Education are taught in many universities; they vary in title - MEd, MA, MSc - according to the academic specialism and tradition of the university.

Entry to these courses may be through certain graduate awards or through Diploma and BEd/BA/BSc awards. There are also opportunities for research in the field of Education leading to the award of Doctor of Philosophy (PhD or DPhil) or a master's degree variously entitled MEd, MA, MSc or MPhil (again according to the field and tradition of the university). A taught doctorate (EdD) is now offered in most universities.

Overseas-trained graduate teachers with teaching experience may, if accepted by a specific school, take up that appointment and simultaneously undertake some training. Details may be obtained from the Teacher Training Agency Teaching Information Line, PO Box 3210, Chelmsford CM1 3WA; Tel: 01245 454454; Fax: 01245 261668.

Courses are arranged under the five headings below. They should be read in conjunction with the article on Teacher Education in the United Kingdom (page VI) which explains the context into which the courses usually fit. Readers with a particular interest in one specialism will find a reference to all courses in the subject area index at the end of the book.

Arrangement of courses:

- **Bachelor Degrees**
- **Certificates and Diplomas**
  Includes the Postgraduate Certificate in Education (PGCE).
- **Master's Degrees**
  Master's Degrees can be taken in one of two ways. This section lists those taken by course work assessed by examinations. Those taken by research followed by a thesis are listed under 'Research Degrees'. However, each method often contains elements of the other and it is almost universal for 'taught' Masters courses to include a dissertation or long essay on a topic studied in depth. There is little distinction among the titles MA, MSc and MEd - the name is a matter for the individual preference of universities.
- **Research Degrees**
  This category covers all degrees consisting of individual research work leading to a published thesis and the taught research degree *Doctor of Education* (EdD). Universities typically offer research facilities across the whole range of Education and their entries can do no more than hint at areas of particular interest.
- **Other Courses**
  Includes short courses, individual study attachments, special or tailor-made courses and other 'non-standard' courses.

NOTE:

- Fees normally apply to the academic year 2001/2002 and may be subject to revision.
- Telephone numbers are given as used within the UK. From abroad this number must usually be prefixed by '0044' and the first '0' of the area code omitted.
- Meanings of acronyms and abbreviations can be found in the Glossary on page XI.

The paragraphs below contain some of the points that readers must bear in mind as they apply for any of the courses in this Compendium. Space does not allow for a discussion of the many social and financial factors that need to be considered before embarking on a course of study in Britain. Readers will find a more thorough coverage in the British Council publication *Studying and Living in Britain.**

Universities in the UK cherish their autonomy. They are individually responsible for validating and awarding their own degrees and setting their own entry standards. Consequently there are no national guidelines by which prospective candidates can assess whether their qualifications will admit them to a particular course of study. Neither is there an agreed system for expressing overseas qualifications in terms of their British equivalents, though some information about the comparability in Britain of overseas academic qualifications may be obtained from NARIC, ECCTIS 2000 Ltd, Oriel House, Oriel Road, Cheltenham GL50 1XP, UK (www.ecctis.co.uk). **Candidates must contact the institutions in which they are interested for a ruling on their individual qualifications.**

Universities have **two types of entry requirement**: There is a general requirement, intended to ensure that a student is competent to pursue studies at university level, for example that he or she has sufficient command of English. Supplementing this are the specific requirements for each course - for example, a course specialising in Special Education Needs may require that students have experience in working with children requiring special education. Most course directors will accept a range of possible entry qualifications, and though these have been summarised in this handbook, intending students should also **consult the prospectuses of individual universities or read *University and College Entrance: Official Guide*.**

The above stresses the variability of admission requirements for courses. It is also important to remember that **entry to university courses in the UK is competitive**; places are limited and even for a student who fulfils all the entrance requirements, there can be no guarantee of a place on a course.

In view of the complexities of admission to university courses, candidates are recommended to **read through this handbook and select courses** that interest them. They should then **contact the respective institutions** for confirmation of their eligibility for the courses and for further information about it. Universities are pleased to answer individual queries and will go to some trouble to ensure that students choose a course that is right for them.

It is essential to **apply well before the course starts**. The academic year begins in September/October, though research students can often start at other times and some non-standard courses run at intervals throughout the year.

Applications for PGCE courses should be made through the **Graduate Teacher Training Registry**, and for **BEd/BA/BSc courses** through the **Universities Central Admissions Service**. The address for both GTTR and UCAS is Rosehill, New Barn Lane, Cheltenham GL52 3LZ. For further details see their websites: www.gttr.ac.uk; www.ucas.ac.uk.

Training bursaries/grants for PGCE students in England and Wales (Primary and Secondary) are available. Most EU students, not already employed as teachers, will also be eligible for this bursary. For details see the TTA website (www.canteach.gov.uk).

See the Further Reading list following this section for details of these and other publications and websites.

These publications are generally available for reference in large public libraries, offices of the British Council and, where there is no British Council office, British Embassies.

Studying and Living in Britain 2001/2002 (ISBN 1860178464)
Published annually by the British Council.
£5.99 (plus postage and handling)
Obtainable from *Plymbridge Distributors Ltd, Plymbridge House, Estover Road, Plymouth PL6 7PY, UK; www.plymbridge.com*

The Official UCAS Guide to University & College Entrance 2003 (book and CD Rom) (ISBN 1-84361-007-8)
Published annually by UCAS.
£24.95 (plus postage and packing)
Obtainable from *UCAS Distribution, PO Bx 130, Cheltenham GL52 3ZF, UK; www.swotbooks.com/ucasbooks*

Study Abroad 2000/01 (ISBN 0119852047)
Published by UNESCO
£17.50 (plus £3.00 handling charge)
Available from *The Stationery Office, 51 Nine Elms Lane, London SW8 5DR, UK; www.clicktso.com*

Commonwealth Universities Yearbook 2001 (ISBN 085143178X)
£180 (£200 airmail)
To staff of ACU member institutions £144 (£164 airmail)
Published by and obtainable from the *Association of Commonwealth Universities, John Foster House, 36 Gordon Square, London WC1H 0PF, UK; www.acu.ac.uk*

International Awards 2001+ (ISBN 0851431763)
£40.00 (£43.00 airmail)
To staff of ACU member institutions £32.00 (£35.00 airmail)
Published by and obtainable from the *Association of Commonwealth Universities, John Foster House, 36 Gordon Square, London WC1H 0PF, UK; www.acu.ac.uk*

Useful websites:
www.gttr.ac.uk
www.ucas.ac.uk
www.dfes.gov.uk
www.canteach.gov.uk
www.universitiesuk.ac.uk
www.scop.ac.uk
www.britcoun.org
www.unesco.org
www.acu.ac.uk
www.prospects.csu.ac.uk
www.hero.ac.uk
www.support4learning.org.uk
www.ecctis.co.uk

A	A-level	Advanced Level
	ACE	Accredited Certificate of Education
	ACPD	Advanced Certificate in Professional Development
	ACU	Association of Commonwealth Universities
	APEL	Accreditation of Prior Experiental Learning
	APL	Accreditation of Prior Learning
	AS	Advanced Subsidiary
	AVCE	Advanced Vocational Certificate of Education
B	BA	Bachelor of Arts
	BEd	Bachelor of Education
	BPhil	Bachelor of Philosophy
	BPS	British Psychological Society
	BSc	Bachelor of Science
	BTEC	Business and Technology Education Council
C	CAPS	Certificate of Advanced Professional Studies
	CASE	Certificate in the Advanced Study of Education
	CATS	Credit Accumulation Transfer Scheme
	Cert	Certificate
	CGLI	City and Guilds of London Institute
	CNAA	Council for National Academic Awards
	CPD	Certificate in Professional Development; *also* Continuing Professional Development
	CPS	Certificate of Professional Studies
	CPSE	Certificate of Professional Studies in Education
D	D&T	Design and Technology
	DASE	Diploma in the Advanced Study of Education
	DEdPsy	Doctor in Educational Psychology
	DELTA	Diploma in English Language Teaching to Adults
	DfEs	Department for Education and Skills
	Dip	Diploma
	DocEdPsych	Doctor in Educational Psychology
	DPhil	Doctor of Philosophy
	DProf	Doctor by Professional Study
E	EdD	Doctor in Education
	ELT	English Language Teaching
	EP	Educational Psychology
	ESOL	English for Speakers of Other Languages
	ESRC	Economic and Social Research Council
	EU	European Union
F	FAHE	Further, Adult and Higher Education
	FE	Further Education
	FENTO	Further Education National Training Organisation
	FHE	Further and Higher Education
	f/t	full-time

G	GCE	General Certificate in Education
	GCSE	General Certificate in School Education
	GNVQ	General National Vocational Qualification
	GBR	Graduate Basis for Registration
	GRB	Graduate Registration Basis
	GTP	Graduate Teacher Programme
	GTTR	Graduate Teacher Training Registry *(Rosehill, New Barn Lane, Cheltenham GL52 3LZ, UK; T: 01242 544788; F: 01242 544962; W: www.gttr.ac.uk)*
H	HE	Higher Education
	HMI	Her Majesty's Inspector/ate
	HNC	Higher National Certificate
	HND	Higher National Diploma
	Hons	Honours
	HRD	Human Resource Development
	HRM	Human Resource Management
I	ICT	Information and Communication Technology
	IELTS	International English Language Test Score
	INSET	Inservice Training of Teachers
	IT	Information Technology
	ITT	Initial Teacher Training
	ITE	Initial Teacher Education
K	K/S	Key Stage
L	LaWP	Learning at Work
	LEA	Local Education Authority
M	MA	Master of Arts
	MALT	Media-Assisted Language Teaching
	MEd	Master of Education
	MFL	Modern Foreign Languages
	MPhil	Master of Philosophy
	MProf	Master by Professional Study
	MRes	Master of Research
	MSc	Master of Science
N	NVQ	National Vocational Qualification
	NCVQ	National Council for Vocational Qualifications *(now incorporated into QCA)*
	NCWBLP	National Centre for Work-based Learning Partnerships
	NGO	Non-Government Organisation
O	ODA	Overseas Development Agency
	OFSTED	Office for Standards in Education
P	pa	per annum
	PCE	Post-compulsory Education
	PE	Physical Education
	PGCE	Postgraduate Certificate in Education
	PGCert	Postgraduate Certificate
	PGCPD	Postgraduate Certificate in Professional Development

	PGDip	Postgraduate Diploma
	PHC	Primary Health Care
	PhD	Doctor of Philosophy
	PSHE	Personal, Social & Health Education
	p/t	part-time
Q	QCA	Qualifications and Assessment Authority
	QTS	Qualified Teacher Status
R	R&D	Research and Development
	RE	Religious Education
	RSA	Royal Society of Arts Examinations Board
S	SEN	Special Educational Needs
	SEDA	Staff and Professional Development Association
	SLD	Severe Learning Difficulties
T	TEFL	Teaching English as a Foreign Language
	TESOL	Teaching English to Speakers of other Languages
	TQM	Total Quality Management
	TTA	Teacher Training Agency
U	UCAS	Universities and Colleges Admissions Services *(Rosehill, New Barn Lane, Cheltenham GL52 3LZ, UK ; T: 01242 227788; F: 01242 221502; W:www.ucas.ac.uk)*
	UK	United Kingdom
	UKCOSA	United Kingdom Council for Overseas Student Affairs *(also called The Council for International Education)*
	UPLS	Upper Primary / Lower Secondary
V	VCE	Vocational Certificate of Education

UNIVERSITIES and COLLEGES

School of Education
Bishop Hall Lane
CHELMSFORD   CM1 1SQ

T: 01245 493131
F: 01245 490835
W: www.apu.ac.uk

Enquiries: Jan Sutton; j.sutton@apu.ac.uk; International Office; T: 01245 493131 x3061

BACHELOR DEGREES

- **BA Hons in Education Studies (with Humanities or Early Childhood Education)**

Length of course: 3 years f/t

Entry requirements: A pass at grade C or above in five subjects at GCSE, one of which must be English Language or equivalent, plus a minimum of 160 points gained through possession of any four AS levels, including at least two taken at A2 level, or at least a grade C in a 12-unit GNVQ award. For the Humanities pathway at least one A2 level must be in English or History or Sociology. (For the Early Childhood Education pathway the BTec Early Childhood Studies may be offered, with a minimum of eight merits.) Applications from mature students (over 21) are welcomed and considered on an individual basis.

Course content: This programme focuses on the structure and processes of education in the national and international contexts. A common core of Education Studies modules in the first year is followed by a range of optional modules in the second and third years to allow a degree of specialisation, although the range of options available at any one time will depend upon group size.

Students taking Humanities will study a range of modules drawn from the subject disciplines of English, History and Sociology. Those taking Early Childhood Education will follow a programme which combines academic study with practical involvement in early childhood settings.

For those who choose to do so, there will be a period of study abroad during the second semester of Year Two. All students will have the opportunity to acquire or further develop proficiency in a modern foreign language, usually French, Spanish or German.

Methods of teaching and learning: Lecture, student-led seminars, directed reading, observation of educational practice and group presentations. Students will draw upon their own experience as learners - and as 'teachers' in informal settings - to inform their studies.

Assessment: Written examination, coursework, oral presentations, enquiry-based project / dissertation.

Enquiries: Dr Leslie Bash; l.bash@apu.ac.uk

- **BA Hons French with Education (Secondary Initial Teacher Training)**

Length of course: 2 years f/t

Entry requirements: Successful completion of one year of higher education in French, GCE A-level or Baccalaureate (or equivalent); GCSE/GCE or equivalent in Maths and English Language at grade C or above; ability to speak and write fluent French and English.

Course content: This modular course is designed to provide competent linguists with a professional training. Specialist subject modules aim to develop language skills and

cultural knowledge through the study of contemporary topics such as:
- Social issues
- The media
- Economic and environmental problems

There are also modules which develop skills in teaching a foreign language to secondary school pupils. The educational and professional studies modules develop a broad understanding of the ways in which schools are organised and the professional role of the teacher in the personal and social education of children. A continuous programme of school-based work is included in addition to block teaching practices.

Assessment: Coursework and written and oral examinations.
Enquiries: Claude Kilgallon; c.kilgallon@apu.ac.uk

■ **BSc Hons Science with Education (Secondary Initial Teacher Training)**

Length of course: 2 years f/t
Entry requirements: Successful completion of one year of higher education in Science or a Higher National Diploma or equivalent; GCE/GCSE or equivalent in Maths and English Language at grade C or above.
Course content: This modular course has four major components:
- Science subject studies
- Application of the subjects to pupils' learning
- Educational and professional studies
- Supervised teaching practice as well as other school experience

There are equal numbers of Biology, Chemistry and Physics modules in the subject studies component in which Earth Science also features. There are modules which examine the basis of the Science curriculum and how the subject can be effectively presented to secondary school pupils. The educational and professional study modules provide students with the support necessary for them to function as competent classroom practitioners.

Assessment: Based on a combination of courses, individual project, written examinations and teaching practice.
Enquiries: Alan Myers; a.myers@apu.ac.uk

■ **BA Hons Primary Education (Initial Teacher Training)**

Length of course: 3 years f/t
Entry requirements: A minimum of 220 points gained through possession of four AS levels with at least three being taken to A2 level, or at least a grade B in a 12-unit GNVQ Advanced award, or at least three Distinctions and five Merits in a BTec award. Applicants over the age of 21 without the above may be considered if they have completed an accredited Access programme, preferably with at least one A2 level at grade C or higher. A GCSE pass at grade C or higher in English Language, Mathematics and Science is not compulsory for applicants born before 1 September 1979, but is desirable. All applicants must have recent experience of working in a UK primary school.
Course content: This is a modular degree appropriate for students wishing to specialise in Primary Education and work with children in the 5-11 age range. It is offered in partnership with selected primary schools in the region and approximately a quarter of the time is spent working in schools. The programme prepares students to teach the

core and foundation subjects of the primary National Curriculum. Modules focus on ICT across the curriculum and on such issues as:

- Assessment of Learning
- Child Development
- Classroom Management
- Primary English
- Primary Foundation Subjects
- Primary Mathematics
- Primary Science
- Teachers' Professional Duties
- Working with Parents

Enquiries: Alison Shilela; a.c.shilela@apu.ac.uk

As the impact of the implementation of current DfES regulations takes effect and in response to future changes in regulations, the University reserves the right to make appropriate changes to the programme.

CERTIFICATES / DIPLOMAS

■ **PGCE Primary**

Length of course: 38 weeks (mid September - mid July)

Entry requirements: UK honours degree or equivalent; GCSE/GCE in English Language and Maths at grade C or above. It is helpful if applicants with Arts degrees also have a GCSE/GCE in a Science subject at grade C or above (as must all applicants who were born on or after 1st September 1979). Applicants will be expected to have experience of working in a UK primary school.

Course content: The programme prepares graduates to specialise in Primary Education and work with children in the 5-11 age range. It is offered in partnership with selected primary schools in the region and approximately half the time is spent working in schools. Students are prepared to teach the core and foundation subjects of the primary National Curriculum and are expected to study the pedagogy of their degree specialism (or related primary curriculum subject) to enable them to offer curriculum leadership in the primary school. Among the issues studied in both theory and practice throughout the programme are:

- ICT across the curriculum
- Child development
- Classroom management
- Assessment of learning
- Working with parents
- Teachers' professional duties

Enquiries: Alison Shilela; a.c.shilela@apu.ac.uk

As the impact of the implementation of current DfES regulations takes effect and in response to future changes in regulations, the University reserves the right to make appropriate changes to the programme.

■ PGCE Secondary

Length of course: 36 weeks

Entry requirements: A UK honours degree or equivalent, which includes a subject specialism in Art, Citizenship, English, History, ICT, MFL, Science; GCSE/GCE English Language and Maths at grade C or above.

Course content: The course has been designed in partnership with secondary schools. Students spend 24 weeks working with pupils in the 11-16 age range in classrooms and are supported by school mentors and specialist subject tutors from the University. During the 12 weeks spent in the University students take a programme designed to further their professional development as teachers.

Enquiries: Caroline Brennan; c.brennan@apu.ac.uk

■ PGCE Post-compulsory Education

Length of course: 2 years p/t (2 modules per semester)

Entry requirements: Entrants must normally be teachers in post-compulsory education or training who already possess the equivalent of an honours degree supplemented by relevant professional experience. Students may be admitted to the programme with credit on the basis of prior certificated learning (APL) and/or assessed experiential learning (APEL).

Course content: Year 1 consists of four modules which lay the practical foundations of teaching in the PCE sector. Year 2 develops deeper understanding of curriculum development, professional development and includes a number of option modules. Both years include a practical teaching element. The course enables both existing and new staff to obtain a teaching qualification.

Enquiries: Gordon Bellamy; g.a.bellamy@apu.ac.uk

MASTER'S DEGREES

■ MA Education

Length of course: 1-6 years p/t

Entry requirements: Entrants must normally be qualified teachers, experienced educationalists or professionals working in an educational context with an UK honours degree or equivalent.

Course content: The MA Education has been designed for the professional development of teachers and others involved in education. There is a wide choice of modules of direct relevance to a range of professional contexts and comprising assessment tasks which are focused on professional practice. Several on-line modules are available. Most modules are taught in the evenings and some during the daytime. The programme is suitable for part-time study.

Enquiries: Scilla Furey; s.furey@apu.ac.uk

■ MA in Teaching & Learning in HE and FE

Length of course: 1 module per semester p/t

Entry requirements: Entrants must normally be teachers in post-compulsory education who already possess the equivalent of an honours degree supplemented by relevant professional experience. Students may be admitted to the programme with credit on the basis of prior certificated learning (APL) and/or accredited experiential learning (APEL).

Course content: The programme consists of three stages:
- Stage 1 leads to a PGCert in Teaching & Learning in HE and FE comprising two modules.
- Stage 2 consists of two further modules with an Action Research focus which, when completed successfully in addition to the Certificate, lead to the award of PGDip in HE and FE. This stage is recognised by the English National Board for Nursing as a suitable qualification for Nurse Teachers (contingent upon completion of specified modules of the programme including Supervised Teaching Experience).
- Stage 3 culminates in the MA degree and consists of either another module chosen from a menu plus a short dissertation or a larger dissertation. The MA follows upon successful completion of the Postgraduate Diploma stage.

Enquiries: Gordon Bellamy; g.a.bellamy@apu.ac.uk

RESEARCH DEGREES

■ MPhil, PhD

Length of course:

MPhil:	18 (min) - 48 (max) months f/t
PhD via transfer:	33 (min) - 60 (max) months f/t
PhD direct:	24 (min) - 60 (max) months f/t

Entry requirements:

MPhil or MPhil with transfer: The international student shall normally hold a first or second class honours degree of a university, of the Council for National Academic Awards, of a university in the UK or a qualification which is regarded by the Research Degrees Committee as equivalent to such an honours degree.

Direct registration for the degree of PhD: Normally requires that the candidate holds a Masters degree in a discipline appropriate to the proposed research awarded as above. For international students there is an additional requirement of English language competence equivalent to IELTS 6.5

Course content: As part of their research, a candidate shall normally follow a programme of related studies:

Induction: Strategies for success as a research student, time and task management, working with supervisors, research methodology, and University services and facilities.

Mid Phase: Academic writing and scholarly publications, seminar and conference presentation.

Final Phase: Thesis production and examination / viva preparation.

Enquiries: Dr Gillian Robinson; g.d.robinson@apu.ac.uk

FEES:

EU students: £1100
Non-EU students: £6850

UNIVERSITY OF BATH

Department of Education
Claverton Down
BATH BA2 7AY

T: 01225 386225
F: 01225 386113
E: education@bath.ac.uk
W: www.bath.ac.uk/education

<u>Head of Department:</u> Dr Andrew Stables

BACHELOR DEGREES

■ BA Hons Coach Education and Sports Development

<u>Length of course:</u> 3 years f/t (an optional year of study abroad or a year of industrial placement is offered between year 2 and 3, bringing the total years of study to 4)

<u>Course aims/content/structure:</u> This course aims to revolutionise and improve the approach to Coach Development in the UK. Students study coaching within the context of both educational theories and current research. Optional units are available in Years 2 and 3(4). A major research project is carried out in the final year.

<u>Assessment:</u> Assignments, presentations, practicals, research projects and exams.

<u>Fees:</u> *EU students:* £1075; *Non-EU students:* £7660

<u>Enquiries/applications:</u> Course Administrator Coach Education *(address see above)*; T: 01225 386012; F: 01225 386113; E: coacheducation@bath.ac.uk

CERTIFICATES / DIPLOMAS

■ Advanced Diploma / Certificate in Education

<u>Length of course:</u>   *Cert:* 1 semester (min) (beginning January or September)
Dip: 2 semesters (min) (beginning January or September)
Part-time study is also available.

In addition to the term-time programme, an intensive programme is offered during an annual Summer School in July which requires attendance at the University.

<u>Entry requirements:</u> Normally a recognised teaching qualification and two years' relevant experience. Candidates do not need to be graduates.

<u>Course content:</u>   *Cert:* Two units plus an extended essay of 6000-8000 words
Dip: Four units plus a mini-dissertation of 8000-10,000 words

Each taught unit consists of 30 hours of discussions, workshops, seminars and formal inputs plus a minimum of 120 hours individual study time. For choice of units available see MA in Education below.

<u>Assessment:</u> Individuals are encouraged to negotiate their assignments, each of which should be 3500-4500 words.

<u>Fees:</u> *Vary according to mode of delivery.*

<u>Enquiries:</u> Director of Studies for Advanced Courses *(address see above)*; T: 01225 386602; F: 01225 386113; E: ed.ma@bath.ac.uk

■ PGCE with recommendation for QTS

<u>Length of course:</u> 1 years f/t

<u>Entry requirements:</u> A relevant degree and equivalent of GCSE grade C or above in English and Maths (for middle years: if born after 1 Sept. 1979 also equivalent of GCSE grade C or above in Science).

<u>Course content/structure:</u> The course involves sessions in the University and extensive experience in local schools. Subjects offered are:

Secondary (11-18): English, Maths, Science (Physics, Chemistry, Biology, Environmental Science, Earth Science), Geography, History, MFL (French, German, Spanish), PE, IT
Middle Years (7-14): English, Maths, Science
Enquiries: Director of Studies for PGCE *(address see beginning of entry)*; T: 01225 386225; F: 01225 386113; E: pgce@bath.ac.uk

MASTER'S DEGREES

■ MA in Education

Candidates for the MA in Education may either opt for the general MA or specialise to obtain an award in one of the following: Educational Technology; Educational Management; Environmental Education; Language in Education; International Education; Learning and Teaching.
Length of course: 12 months f/t (beginning January or September); p/t also available
In addition to the term-time programme, an intensive programme is offered during an annual Summer School in July which requires attendance at the University.
Entry requirements: Normally a recognised teaching qualification and two years' relevant experience. Candidates do not necessarily need to be graduates.
Course content: Six units plus a dissertation of 20,000 words. Each taught unit consists of 30 hours of discussions, workshops, seminars and formal inputs plus a minimum of 120 hours study time. Details of unit titles available on request. Some units are offered by distance learning.
Assessment: Six assignments of 3500 - 4500 words.
Fees: Full-time: *EU students:* £3200; *Non-EU students:* £7660
        Part-time: *Vary according to mode of delivery.*
Enquiries: Director of Studies for Advanced Courses *(address see beginning of entry)*; T: 01225 386602; F: 01225 386113; E: ed.ma@bath.ac.uk

■ MA/Certificate in Education Disability & Rehabilitation (by distance)

Length of course: 2 years (min) f/t by distance learning
Entry requirements: There are no formal entry requirements.
Course content: Distance learning students have access to a learning facilitator to support their study. The following four units must be completed, plus a dissertation of 20,000 words: Experience of Disability, Rehabilitation for Life, Managing Expectations, Independent Study.
Assessment: Each unit is assessed by means of the following components: a portfolio (1000 words); a project report (1000 words); a reflective evaluation (3000 words)
For the award of MA, a dissertation of 20,000 words must also be completed.
Fees: *EU students:* £3200; *Non-EU students:* £7660
Enquiries: Director of Studies; T: 01225 386564; F: 01225 386113; E: dare@bath.ac.uk

■ MA in English Language Teaching (ELT)

Length of course: 1 year f/t or p/t by credit accumulation (max 10 years)
Entry requirements: First degree or equivalent; 2 years f/t experience in teaching English as a foreign language to adults; near native-speaker competence in English.
Course content: The following must be completed: Diploma in English Language Teaching to Adults (DELTA); 2 units from the MA in Education suite relating to Language in Education; 2 further units from the MA in Education; dissertation of about

20,000 words grounded in English Language Teaching.
Assessment: There are 3 components to the DELTA assessment: Coursework; an extended assignment; a written examination. MA units are each assessed by an assignment of about 4000 words; CALL is assessed by a 1500-word essay.
Fees: EU students: £3895; Non-EU students: £7665
Enquiries: Director of Studies for Advanced Courses (address see beginning of entry); T: 01225 386602; F: 01225 386113; E: ed.ma@bath.ac.uk

RESEARCH DEGREES

■ MPhil, PhD, Master of Research (Education)
Length of course: MPhil: 1 year f/t (min); MRes: 1 year f/t (min); PhD: 2 years f/t (min)
Entry requirements:
Either a degree of this or an approved university
or a recognised graduate equivalent qualification
or an Advanced Diploma in Education and two years of relevant experience in education.
PhD students are normally required to register for an MPhil degree initially; transfer to PhD can be made after satisfactory progress.
Course content: MPhil students are required to complete a 60,000 word thesis, PhD students a 100,000 word thesis. An extensive course of research training is provided. Overseas students may carry out fieldwork in their own country, although the department cannot guarantee to fund such fieldwork.
Fees: EU students: £3200 f/t; £1600 p/t; Non-EU students: £7660 f/t; £3830 p/t

■ EdD
Length of course: 2 years (min) f/t; 4 years (min) p/t
Entry requirements: A degree of this or an approved university (or graduate-equivalent status); an advanced qualification (eg Master's degree) in education or a related field; at least two years of appropriate professional experience.
Candidates who meet the criteria except for the advanced qualification may be admitted to the degree following the successful completion of two units from the Department Masters programme.
Course content/structure: The programme comprises the study of four units and the completion of a personal research enquiry. There are two core units: Educational Policy: Theory & Practice; Educational Research: Philosophy & Practice
Candidates then take two further units from the following: Learning about Learning; Leadership for Learning; International Education: Philosophy & Practice; Comparative Approaches to Educational Development; Educational Management; Assessment & Evaluation for Learning: Politics, Philosophy & Practice; Language, Culture & Education; Values; Curriculum, Philosophy & Practice.
There are a number of alternative routes through the EdD programme for suitably qualified candidates. Details are available on application.
Assessment: The units are assessed by means of 8000-word assignments; the research enquiry is assessed by a 40,000-word thesis.
Fees: £981 per unit; £5635 for the research enquiry
Enquiries/applications: Director of Studies (address see beginning of entry); T: 01225 386545; F: 01225 386113; E: ed.doc@bath.ac.uk

Graduate School of Education
69/71 University Street
BELFAST BT7 1HL

T: 028 9033 5941
F: 028 9023 9263
E: education@qub.ac.uk
W: www.qub.ac.uk/edu

<u>Head of School:</u> Ms Ruth Leitch

CERTIFICATES / DIPLOMAS / MASTER'S DEGREES

■ PGCE

<u>Length of course:</u> 36 weeks

<u>Entry requirements:</u> Applicants should be graduates of a recognised university or equivalent institution of higher education and must also have passes at grade C or above in Maths and English Language in the General Certificate of Secondary Education or hold equivalent qualifications.

<u>Course content:</u> Students spend 24 weeks gaining practical experience in schools. The rest of the course, in the Graduate School of Education, centres on a main subject chosen from:

- English
- Maths / IT
- Modern Languages (French, German, Irish, Spanish)
- Science (Biology, Chemistry, Physics)
- Social Sciences (Politics, RE, Sociology)

There are also core areas on Curriculum & Assessment, Learning & Development and Contemporary Educational Issues.

<u>Assessment:</u> There are no formal examinations, but students must pass in practical teaching and coursework (which may include a class test). Successful candidates will be able to obtain recognition to teach in the UK.

<u>Fees:</u> EU students: £1075 pa
      Non-EU students: £7315 pa

<u>Enquiries:</u> Dr Peter Neil *(contact details see above)*

■ MSc
■ MEd
■ Diploma in the Advanced Study of Education (DASE)
■ Advanced Certificate in Education

<u>Length of courses:</u> normally up to 5 years (max) p/t; 1 year f/t

<u>Entry requirements:</u> Honours degree in Education from a recognised university or an honours degree together with an approved qualification in education plus at least two years' professional experience in an education or training context. Other appropriate educational qualifications will be considered.

<u>Course content:</u>

- Art Therapy (MSc)
- Autistic Spectrum Disorders (MSc)
- Educational Studies (MEd)
- Educational Management (MEd)
- Educational Psychology (MEd)
- International Studies in Education (MSc)

- Personal & Civic Education (MSc)
- Primary Education (MEd)
- Special Educational Needs (MSc)
- Severe/Complex Special Needs (MSc)
- Teaching Learners who are Visually Impaired (MSc)

Assessment:
MSc, MEd: Successful accumulation of 120 M-points and a 15-20,000-word dissertation.
DASE: Successful accumulation of 120 M-points.
Advanced Certificate: Successful accumulation of 60 M points.
Fees: EU students: £290/£435 per module
　　　　Non-EU students: £7530 pa (f/t)
Enquiries: Dr John Johnston; E: inserv.edu@qub.ac.uk

RESEARCH DEGREES

■ EdD

This taught doctorate provides an innovative extension to the Graduate School of Education's well established programme of courses. The EdD has three strands: Management & Policy; Educational Studies; Counselling, Psychology & Special Needs. The EdD provides an alternative to the current PhD route for educationalists and will offer a substantive and doctoral-level quality research activity. Applicants may be considered for credit transfer to the EdD for previously completed masters degrees.

Length of course: 3 years (min) f/t; 4 years p/t
Entry requirements: Recognised primary degree; appropriate higher level qualification and at least five years' appropriate experience.
Course structure: The programme comprises nine taught modules (270 D Points), presented in intensive blocks amounting to 30 hours contact time (usually over three days, Thursday to Saturday) and a dissertation (270 D Points).
Assessment: Written assignments and dissertation.
Fees: EU students: £405 per module
　　　Non-EU students: £7530 pa f/t
Enquiries: Professor Tony Gallagher *(contact details see beginning of entry)*

■ MPhil, PhD

Length of course: *MPhil:* 1 year f/t; 3 years p/t
　　　　　　　　　PhD: 3 years f/t; 4 years p/t
Entry requirements: Good honours degree together with a professional diploma or equivalent.
Research areas: All areas related to educational research.
Assessment: Successful completion of a thesis.
Fees: EU students: £2805 pa f/t; £950 pa p/t
　　　Non-EU students: £7530 f/t and p/t
Enquiries: Professor Jannette Ellwood *(contact details see beginning of entry)*

School of Education
Edgbaston
BIRMINGHAM   B15 2TT

T: 0121 414 3967
F: 0121 414 4865
E: m.e.tait@bham.ac.uk
W: www.bham.ac.uk

Enquiries: Professor Lynn Davies, Director; Centre for International Education & Research; l.davies@bham.ac.uk; T: 0121 414 4823

The School of Education has a long-standing interest in the study of education in an international context. It contains a Centre for International Education and Research which mounts courses specifically relating to education world-wide, co-ordinates programmes which include overseas participants across the range of courses mounted by the School and provides support services such as study skills courses, a programme of visits to schools and other institutions, additional English language tuition where necessary and help with individual student welfare. Course participants from overseas also attend lectures in common with serving teachers and senior personnel from Britain on in-service courses and thus have an opportunity of sharing experience and mutual concerns with them. The recently enlarged School now has two large specialist Education libraries, together with computer and science laboratories.
It also houses five specialist centres:
• Schools Inspection Unit
• Centre for Research in Medical & Dental Education (CRMDE)
• Centre for Sociocultural & Activity Theory Research (CSAT)
• Visual Impairment Centre for Teaching & Research (VICTAR)
• Centre for International Education & Research (CIER)
There are close links with Birmingham Local Education Authority and other LEAs in the immediate vicinity. Attachments for course participants and visitors can therefore be arranged in a wide variety of programmes of study: inspection, planning, finance, educational administration, primary, secondary and further education, or special education.
Major research strengths in the School of Education are in the fields of:
• Educational Planning & Management
• Languages & Literature
• Science, Maths & Technological Education
• Religious Education
• Special Education
A range of international research work (eg Decentralisation, Democracy, Special Education, Gender) has been undertaken.
The specific welfare, social and language needs and interests of course participants from overseas are specially provided for in the university through such agencies and personnel as the International Office, Director of International Affairs, the Adviser to Overseas Students, and the English for International Students Unit. The Accommodation and Welfare Office has a permanent officer specifically appointed to deal with accommodation for overseas students and visitors. Mature students are usually accommodated in University-owned self-catering flats or in international guest houses. Advice and social facilities for international students are also provided by the Guild of

Students (Students' Union). The University Campus provides dining, health, sports, religious and shopping facilities necessary for a community of 20,000 students and 1400 academic staff. The University has over 3000 international students each year.

BACHELOR DEGREES

■ BPhil
Length of course: 12 months f/t
Entry requirements: Professional qualifications or the equivalent of 240 credits obtained after the equivalent of a 2-year full-time programme of study; 2 years relevant professional experience.
Course content: Candidates complete four modules (course sub-sections) from either a specified Programme of Study (see below) or to form a General Programme of Study.
Assessment: Continuous assessment of coursework in each of the modules selected; a dissertation on a relevant topic, not normally exceeding 10,000 words.
Fees: EU students: £1500
      Non-EU students: £7400

CERTIFICATES / DIPLOMAS

■ Diploma
Length of course: 1 year f/t
Entry requirements:
Either a degree of an approved university or diplomas
or   other qualifications judged satisfactory and 2 years' relevant professional
        experience
or   5 years' relevant professional experience and an appropriate educational
        background.
Course content: Candidates complete six modules which normally include one project module either from a specified Programme of Study or from a General Programme of Study (see below).
Assessment: Continuous assessment or formal examinations.
Fees: EU students: £1500
      Non-EU students: £7400

■ Advanced Certificate in Education / Postgraduate Certificate in Education
Length of course: 1 semester f/t or its equivalent
Entry requirements: Professional qualifications or the equivalent of 240 credits obtained after the equivalent of a 2-year full-time programme of study; 2 years' relevant professional experience; for PGCert a first degree.
Course content: Candidates complete three modules, which normally include one project module either specialising in one Programme of Study or choosing from the range of modules provided in the School (see below).
Assessment: Continuous assessment.
Fees: EU students: £750
      Non-EU students: £3700

MASTER'S DEGREES

■ MEd

Length of course: 12 months f/t

Entry requirements: A degree of an approved university or diplomas or other qualifications judged satisfactory for this purpose; successful completion of a professional training programme; two years' relevant professional experience.

Course content: Candidates complete five modules either from a specified Programme of Study or from a General Programme of Study *(see below)* and also complete the compulsory Research methods module and a research dissertation.

Assessment: This will normally be by continuous assessment of coursework in each of the modules selected. In addition to the coursework, candidates will submit a dissertation on a relevant topic, not normally exceeding 15,000 words.

Fees: EU students: £2250
        Non-EU students: £7400

The MA in Education has similar course requirements, but does not need previous professional experience, and contains a programme of school observation in UK.

Programmes of Study:

- *Information Technology in Education* - Modules: Computer-based learning; computers in educational administration; IT and computing curricula; problem solving; computers in society.
- *The Management of Special Education in Developing Countries* - Modules: School observation, evaluation and supervision; practical management in contexts of stringency; equity and efficiency in the management of schools; SEN - support for learning; advising and consultancy in special education.
- *International Management & Policy in Education* - Modules: Educational policy in national development; practical management in contexts of stringency;   human rights and citizenship; personal skills for women and men in educational management; curriculum innovation; school observation, evaluation and supervision; leadership.
- *Language* - Modules: Learning mechanisms in the acquisition of a new foreign language; communicative style teaching and learning in foreign languages; bilingualism; TEFL.
- *Special Education (Learning Difficulties, moderate and severe learning difficulties)* - Modules: Policy and provision for special needs; assessment and curriculum teaching and learning for pupils with learning difficulties.
- *Special Education (Autism)* - Modules: Special needs, curriculum and approaches for pupils with autism.
- *Special Education (Dyslexia)* - Modules: Identification, assessment and teaching for pupils with specific learning difficulties.
- *Special Education (Speech and Language Difficulties)* - Modules: Introduction to speech and language difficulties.
- *Special Education (Emotional and Behaviour Difficulties)* - Modules: Emotional and behaviour difficulties; improving classroom achievement; guidance counsellors.
- *Special Education (Learning Support)* - Modules: Meeting the needs of pupils with special educational needs in mainstream schools, improving classroom achievement.

- *Special Education (Hearing Impaired)* - Modules: Development and teaching of deaf and hearing impaired children.
- *Special Education (Visually Impaired)* - These are self-contained programmes, designed for teachers currently, or expecting to be, working with children in the respective specialised fields. The courses aim to provide a sound understanding of the nature and effects of the impairment and the knowledge and skills necessary for assessment and effective teaching.
- *Religious Education* - Modules: Recent developments in RE; methods of teaching RE; Islamic education; the religious education of women and girls.

RESEARCH DEGREES

■ MPhil(Ed), PhD, EdD

<u>Length of course:</u> *MPhil:*   1 year (min) f/t
             PhD/EdD: 2 years (min) f/t; 3 years (min) p/t external*

<u>Entry requirements:</u>
MPhil: Approved degree or diploma; teacher education; 2 years' professional experience (some exemptions granted).
PhD: First class honours degrees or Masters degree.
<u>Course content:</u> Enquiries are welcomed from candidates wishing to pursue research in most areas of educational enquiry. Current EdD routes are in the fields of:

- Educational Leadership
- Educational Disadvantage & SEN
- Language Studies
- International Management & Policy

Research Methods courses by distance and a certificate in Research Methods are available. Overseas students may, where appropriate, spend part of their registration period pursuing fieldwork in their own countries.
<u>Fees:</u> EU students: £2805
       Non-EU students: £7400
* *Students are based in their own country but spend a minimum of six months in Birmingham during the period of their registration (this need not be continuous).*

OTHER COURSES

■ Short Courses / Fellowships
Non-award-bearing short courses and fellowships are provided for Inspectors, Headteachers, Senior Educationists and Ministry personnel. These may be individually-designed courses and attachments to suit particular needs and can be mounted in-country where appropriate, or on a split-site basis.

Bishop Grosseteste College
LINCOLN LN1 3DY

T: 01522 527347
F: 01522 530243
E: registry@bgc.ac.uk
W: www.bgc.ac.uk

<u>Head of Department:</u> Dr Derek Bell, Vice-Prinicipal
<u>Contact person:</u> Karen Booth; k.g.booth@bgc.ac.uk

BACHELOR DEGREES

- **BA/BSc Combined Studies Programme with linked PGCE with recommendation for QTS**
  Degrees available:
  BA Hons Art & Design and Education Studies
  BA Hons Drama and Education Studies
  BA Hons English and Education Studies
  BA Hons Geography and Education Studies
  BA Hons History and Education Studies
  BA Hons Music and Education Studies
  BA Hons Religious Studies and Education Studies
  BSc Hons Mathematics and Education Studies
  BSc Hons Studies in Science and Education Studies
  <u>Length of course:</u> 3 years undergraduate plus 1 year postgraduate (PGCE)
  <u>Entry requirements:</u> Normally GCSE English Language, Maths at grade C or above (Science for those born on or after 1 September 1979); A-level CC or equivalent, including Main Subject; recent and relevant experience in a primary classroom. Mature entrants or those with alternative qualifications, please contact the Registry.
  <u>Course content:</u> School placements, primary curriculum, organisation and management of children's learning, main subject related work, etc.
  <u>Assessment:</u> continuous

- **BA Hons Primary Education with recommendation for QTS**
  <u>Length of course:</u> 3 years f/t
  <u>Entry requirements:</u> GCSE English Language, Maths at grade C or above (Science for those born on or after 1 September 1979); A-level CC or equivalent, including English or Maths; recent and relevant experience in a primary classroom. Mature entrants, please contact the Registry.
  <u>Course content:</u> Teacher training in the age range of 4-11, studying six National Curriculum subjects and application.
  <u>Assessment:</u> continuous

- **BA Hons Drama in the Community**
  <u>Length of course:</u> 3 years f/t
  <u>Entry requirements:</u> A-level DD or equivalent to include Drama and practical involvement in Drama. Mature entrants or those with alternative qualifications, please contact the Registry.
  <u>Course content:</u> Semester and project studies examine the role and contributions of drama in a range of contemporary contexts.
  <u>Assessment:</u> continuous

■ **BA Hons Heritage Studies**
Length of course: 3 years f/t
Entry requirements: A-level DD or equivalent and some experience or interest in the subject. Mature entrants or those with alternative qualifications, please contact the Registry.
Course content: Modular programme with a vocational element, practical preparation alongside academic study and research, work placement, etc.
Assessment: continuous

■ **BA Hons English Literature**
Length of course: 3 years f/t
Entry requirements: A-level CD or equivalent - must include English at grade C or above. Mature entrants or those with alternative qualifications, please contact the Registry.
Course content: Mix of six modules covering: Critical Skills, the Literary Canon, New Writing, etc.
Assessment: continuous

CERTIFICATES / DIPLOMAS

■ **PGCE Primary (full-time)**
Length of courses: 1 year f/t
Entry requirements: GCSE English Language, Maths at grade C or above (Science for those born on or after 1 September 1979); normally at least a 2.2 honours degree, with significant elements of National Curriculum subjects (normally 50% of degree content should be relevant to the National Curriculum); recent British primary school work experience.
Course content: School placements, primary curriculum, organisation and management of children's learning, lectures, seminars and workshops.
Assessment: continuous
Enquiries: *see beginning of entry*

■ **PGCE Primary (flexible route)**
Length of courses: from 3 months to 3 years (maximum)
Entry requirements: GCSE English Language, Maths at grade C or above (Science for those born on or after 1 September 1979); normally at least a 2.2 honours degree, with significant elements of National Curriculum subjects (normally 50% of degree content should be relevant to the National Curriculum); recent British primary school work experience.
Course content: Students undertake an audit of study needs on entry which provides the basis for their own training plan. The pattern of study will vary, but students are encouraged to join the f/t course for two sessions, spend one day a week in school and at least one other day on directed tasks.
Assessment: continuous
Enquiries: *see beginning of entry*

■ **PGCE Secondary**

Length of courses: 1 year f/t

Entry requirements: GCSE English Language, Maths at grade C or above (Science for those born on or after 1 September 1979); normally at least a 2.2 honours degree relevant to one of the six specialist subject areas; recent British seondary school work experience.

Course content: School placements, classroom management and communication, using and adapting ICT, National Strategies, reforms to 16+ education, cross-curricular themes, out of school activities, special issues placement. Specialist subjects studies in: Art & Design, English with Drama, Music, Religious Studies, Science, Maths.

Course structure: *Phase I:* Course and placement school introduction; skills audit

Phase II/III: Specialist subject learning; teaching and assessment

Phase IV/V: Developing classroom skills; pupil, curriculum, school & society

Phase VI: Special issue project; placement

Assessment: continuous

Enquiries: *see beginning of entry*

■ **Certificate in Professional Studies in Education (CPSE)**
■ **Diploma in Professional Studies in Education (DPSE)**

Length of courses: normally 1 year p/t CPSE; 2 years p/t DPSE

Entry requirements: Teaching qualification and experience.

Course content: Modular programme.

Assessment: Assignment and viva voce examination.

Enquiries: Harriet Marland; eds@bgc.ac.uk

MASTER'S DEGREES

■ **MA in Education Primary**

Length of course: 2 years p/t

Entry requirements: Teaching qualification and minimum 3 years' experience.

Course content: Taught modular programme on current educational issues.

Assessment: Assignment and dissertation.

Enquiries: Harriet Marland; eds@bgc.ac.uk

FEES: *Contact College for details.*

BOLTON INSTITUTE OF HIGHER EDUCATION

Education Subject Group
Faculty of Arts, Sciences and Education
Chadwick Street
BOLTON   BL2 1JW

T: 01204 528851/900600
F: 01204 399074
E: enquiries@bolton.ac.uk
W: www.bolton.ac.uk

The Education Subject Group is a specialist centre for technical and vocational teacher education and training. It is housed in modern, purpose-built accommodation which includes a well-stocked library and learning resources centre, computing and information technology centre, laboratories, building and engineering workshops, all designed for the preparation of teaching materials and practising teaching methods. Most of the staff have had wide experience of working alongside people from overseas countries and, in the last 20 years, projects or consultancies have taken place in 28 countries outside Europe.

BACHELOR DEGREES

■ BEd in Technical & Vocational Education & Training

Length of course: 12 months (September start)
Entry requirements: Approved Certificate in Education or equivalent.
Course content: The course seeks to develop competence in:
• the processes of curriculum development and evaluation
• identifying and responding to issues arising from the management of the curriculum and curriculum change and the management of vocational education and training institutions
Flexibility to cater for individual needs is achieved through the modular structure. The Institute has experience of delivering this programme in a host country.
Fees: £6300, including registration

CERTIFICATES / DIPLOMAS

■ PGCE

This initial training course is intended for those teaching, or intending to teach, in the field of technical and vocational education to students in the post-compulsory sector of education.
Length of course: 36 weeks (September to June)
Entry requirements: Approved degree or equivalent; appropriate industrial, commercial or professional experience.
Course content: Teaching method courses are available in:
• Adult Basic Education
• Art & Design
• Construction & the Built Environment
• Business Studies (professional and secretarial)
• Catering & Hospitality Management
• Community Education & Lifelong Learning
• Engineering (automobile, chemical, civil, mechanical electronic)
• General Studies (History, Geography, Media Studies, Languages, English, Politics, Drama)

- Hairdressing & Beauty Therapy
- Health & Childhood Studies
- Law & Public Services
- Leisure & Tourism
- Management
- Maths & Computing
- Pure & Applied Sciences
- Social Science
- Sports Science
- Textiles
- Nursing & Related Health Care Subjects

The course includes an assessable component of practical teaching on attachment in local institutions.

Fees: £6800, including registration

■ **Certificate in Education**

This is a parallel version of the PGCE (also lasting 36 weeks) and is suitable for non-graduates whose qualifications are in a teaching subject in which the normal professional qualification is not a degree or equivalent, eg craft engineering or building subjects, hairdressing, catering.

MASTER'S DEGREES

- ■ **MEd Professional Development**
- ■ **MEd Technical & Vocational Education**
- ■ **MA Educational Management**
- ■ **MA Inclusive Education**

The scheme is intended for experienced lecturers, administrators and managers and is suitable for those already in positions of responsibility in education as well as those preparing for such positions.

Length of course: 12 months f/t (January or September start)

Entry requirements: Approved degree or Advanced Diploma and appropriate experience.

Course content: The generic award is an MEd Professional Development. However, course members can achieve the named awards by undertaking specific optional modules in addition to the core. Core modules in Curriculum, Organisational Management and Research provide a broad foundation for further study. The course places emphasis on the wide range of issues involved in the management of technical and vocational education and training institutions or from inclusive education, depending on the routes selected.

Support for study skills is available within the Scheme and for those wishing to improve and develop their range of IT skills a basic course is available at a small extra cost.

Assessment: By course work and dissertation.

Fees: £6800, including registration

RESEARCH DEGREES

■ **MPhil, PhD**

Length of course: MPhil: 12 months (min) in addition to any prescribed period of supportive studies.

PhD: 24 months (min) after transfer from MPhil or 36 months (min) for direct entrants

Entry requirements: Taught Master's degree in Education and evidence of ability and aptitude to undertake research. Applicants may be required to undertake courses in Research Methods in Education. Applications for direct entry to PhD will only be considered from those who already possess a Master's degree obtained by research in Education or a related discipline.

Fees: £6730 including registration

OTHER COURSES

■ **Short Courses and Attachments**

Non-award bearing courses in any area of our work can be provided on request. These courses may vary in length from a few days to several months and can incorporate industrial placements and visits to other institutions. At the request of governments or aid agencies, these courses can be provided in a client's own country if required. A Certificate of Attendance is issued on completion.

Faculty of Education and Sport
Falmer
BRIGHTON BN1 9PH

T: 01273 600900
F: 01273 643407
E: school.of.education@brighton.ac.uk
W: www.brighton.ac.uk

Dean of Faculty: Mr P Griffiths BEd, MA, MSc

Based on two campuses - in purpose-built accommodation at Falmer just outside the cosmopolitan town of Brighton and in beautiful Edwardian buildings in elegant East-bourne - the Faculty comprises three Schools
• The Chelsea School (Eastbourne)
• School of Education (Falmer)
• School of Languages (Falmer)

Both campuses benefit from specialist facilities including information and learning resource centres. Falmer also boasts a language laboratory and media centre and in teacher education a curriculum suite offering resources in Literacy, Maths, Modern Languages, Science and the Humanities, Religious Education, Design Technology and Business Studies in teacher education - all with national recognition and supported by specialist computer workshop facilities. The Chelsea School also has specialist facilities including gymnasium, swimming pool, human performance laboratories, dance studios and a new sports hall and swimming pool.

Special provision for international students at the University of Brighton now includes a residential pre-course induction programme, specialist welfare advice, guaranteed accommodation in Halls of Residence (for early applicants) and English language provision. An International Students Guide is also available.

The Faculty offers a range of over thirty courses ranging from Certificate, Diploma, Bachelor and Master's degrees through to doctoral studies. The undergraduate awards are organized into a modular scheme and the masters programme is now offered on a modular credit accumulation scheme basis.

BACHELOR DEGREES

■ BA Hons with QTS*

Length of course: 2 years f/t

Course content: This shortened initial teacher education course prepares students to teach their specialist subject in schools and colleges. Students spend approximately 50% of the course in school studying alongside a school mentor. At the university students choose from a variety of modules designed to build on their previous experience and learning. All students take Education and Professional Studies modules.

Subject areas available:
• Business Education
• D&T Education
• IT Education
• Maths Education
• MFL Education
• Science Education

■ **BA Hons with QTS***

Length of course: 4 years f/t

Entry requirements: In addition to course specific and standard entry requirements of 2 A-levels or equivalent, students will need a GCSE or equivalent pass in Maths and English language and Science for Primary.

Course content: This course qualifies students as strong classroom practitioners. To ensure this outcome, professional studies, subject studies and school experience are developed together. Primary students qualify with one subject specialism. Secondary students are qualified to teach their specialist subject in secondary schools and colleges to GCSE and A-level. UPLS (Upper Primary/Lower Secondary) students are qualified to teach their specialist subject in the 7-14 age range and also the Primary core curriculum. Professional modules explore issues specific to teaching, examining teaching and learning methods, the changing needs of the school curriculum and special needs. Areas available:

• Secondary D&T
• Primary Education
• Secondary PE
• UPLS - with Maths, Science, MFL, D&T, RE, PE, English, IT

Enquiries: Mrs Maggie Carroll, Head of School of Education; m.carroll@brighton.ac.uk

■ **BA Hons Professional Education Studies****
■ **BA Hons Religious Education Studies****

Length of course: 2-5 years p/t

Course content: These courses are specially designed for experienced professionals. They allow for accreditation for prior learning and for individually negotiated pathways to reflect particular needs. They do not carry QTS. Stage 1 consists of an introductory module. Stage 2 includes two elective modules and a research methods module which helps students plan their enquiry.

Entry requirements: Normally a Certificate in Education, Certificate of Further Education or equivalent.

Enquiries: Mrs Alison Atkinson; a.atkinson@brighton.ac.uk

CERTIFICATES / DIPLOMAS / MASTER'S DEGREES

■ **Certificate/Diploma in Higher Education****
■ **Diploma in Religious Education****
■ **Diploma in HE in Youth & Community****
■ **Postgraduate Certificate in Professional Education Studies****
■ **MA Education****
■ **PGCert / PGDip / MA Academic Practice****

Length of course: 2 or 3 years p/t, 1 year f/t

Course content: These modular certificates, diplomas and degrees meet the changing professional needs of school teachers, lecturers and other professionals engaged in education and training. The structure allows students to choose elective modules from two fields of study. The first field is the professional enquiry whilst electives in the second are syllabus-led, subject-based modules. The subjects currently available are:

- Art & Design
- Early Years Education
- IT
- Language & Literacy
- Education Management
- Maths
- PE
- Science
- Special Needs

(New subjects are added regularly.)

Entry requirements: Normally an honours degree or recognised diploma of appropriate standard.

Enquiries: Mrs Alison Atkinson, School of Education; a.atkinson@brighton.ac.uk

The MA Education has a bespoke variant delivered to professionals in Mauritius.

■ **PGCE Primary and Secondary**

Length of course: 1 year f/t (Secondary 36 weeks; Primary 38 weeks); flexible mode

Entry requirements: A relevant degree or equivalent and GCSE passes at grade C or above in Maths and English Language and Science for Primary.

Course content: Secondary subjects include:

- Art & Design
- Business
- Dance
- D&T
- English
- Geography
- IT
- Maths
- MFL
- PE
- RE
- Science

Two-year conversion courses in D&T, IT, Maths and Science are also available.

Fees: EU students: £1075
      Non-EU students: Band 1: £6990
                   Band 2: £8190

Enquiries: Mrs Maggie Carroll, Head of School of Education; m.carroll@brighton.ac.uk

■ **PGDip / MA in Media-Assisted Language Teaching (MALT)**
■ **PGDip / MA in TESOL**

Length of course: 1 year f/t; 2-6 years p/t

Entry requirements: A first degree, two years' teaching experience and IELTS 7.0.

Course content: These modular degrees provide opportunities for language teachers to update and extend their professional knowledge and skills. Students on both courses follow core modules in areas of applied linguistics and professional investigation. The MA in MALT offers specialisation in the area of computer-based technologies, media analysis and video in language teaching, while the MA in TESOL equips

EFL teachers for fulfilling roles of responsibility within learning environments, such as teacher education, course design and management.
Enquiries: Ms Elspeth Broady; e.a.broady@brighton.ac.uk; T: 01273 643360

■ **Diploma in TESOL**
Length of course: 1 year f/t; 2 years p/t
Course content: This is for those who wish to obtain recognised training in order to teach English as a second language in the private and public sectors, both in the UK and abroad. The focus is on developing skills in methodology and classroom management, underpinned by relevant theory. Every effort is made to personalise the programme to enable participants to specialise in the areas of teaching most appropriate for their needs and background.
Enquiries: Ms Angela Pickering; a.pickering@brighton.ac.uk

* This Initial Teacher Training course falls within the framework of our modular programme designed to offer choice and flexibility.
** This taught post-experience course falls within the framework of a credit accumulation-based modular scheme known as the Professional Development Award Scheme designed for teacher practitioners and those concerned with CPD.

RESEARCH DEGREES

■ **MPhil/PhD, EdD**
The Faculty provides a thriving and stimulating research environment in which to study for MPhil/PhD degrees. A professional doctorate EdD has recently been validated, facilitating the development of the researching professional with educational responsibilities.
On the *Falmer Campus*, the *Education Research Centre* research groups specialise in:
• Literacy in Education (including cultural facilitation of learning, development of literacy, digital literacies)
• Teaching & Learning in Schools (including social pedagogy of classrooms, pupil groups and curriculum applications)
• Higher & Further Education (including policy development, pedagogy and professional degrees)
• Cultural & Religious Issues in Education
• Teaching & Learning of English in International Contexts (especially drawing on digital technologies)
• Research approaches include national and international studies supported through a variety of research methods.
Particular research emphases include:
• Equal Opportunities
• Multi-cultural Issues in Education
• Action-research Frameworks
The *Chelsea School Research Centre*, on the *Eastbourne Campus*, incorporates specialist research units and groups concerned with:
• Curriculum & Youth Sport/Dance Research
• Human Performance

- Sport & Leisure Research

The School has mode A approval as a research training outlet for the Economic and Social Research Council (ESRC) for both part-time and full-time studentships. Research groups are currently working on:

- Cultural analysis of leisure
- Sport and physical education in gender and media contexts
- Psychology of sport performance
- Physiology and sport and exercise
- Sport, leisure and recreation policy and developments

Length of course: *MPhil:* 18 months (min) f/t; 30 months (min) p/t
                 PhD: 24 months (min) f/t: 36 months (min) p/t
                 EdD: 48 months (min) p/t

Entry requirements: Normally first degree qualifications; applications will also be considered on the basis of substantial appropriate experience.

Fees: EU students: £2740 f/t; £1200 p/t
     Non-EU students: £6800 or £7950 (depending upon discipline) f/t
                       (p/t fees on application)
     Research studentships: nil

Full-time studentships are encouraged and financial support, in the form of tuition fee waivers and scholarships, may be available.

Enquiries:

- Professor Alan Tomlinson, Head of Chelsea School Research Centre, Chelsea School, Hillbrow, Eastbourne; a.tomlinson@brighton.ac.uk
- Professor Peter Kutnick, Head of Education Research Centre, *(address see beginning of entry)*; p.kutnick@brighton.ac.uk

OTHER COURSES

■ Tailor-made Courses

The Faculty can provide tailor-made courses for individuals or groups in any areas of our work. Recent examples include:

- Language & Literacy
- Early Childhood Education
- SEN
- Modern Languages & Linguistics
- Management Training
- Religious Studies
- Curriculum Development / Assessment
- Dance
- Drama
- Teaching Taster Courses
- Art & Design
- History & British Culture

■ **US Program (for North American students)**

MA Summer School - A five-week programme providing the opportunity to achieve six credits at Masters level which will be accepted by home universities on a 'transferring-in' basis. Classes are of particular interest to teachers and educationalists and include input on British culture and the British educational system. Teaching modes include a mix of lectures, seminars and workshops with an emphasis on small group work. A Field Trip package is also available.

Undergraduate Programme - The University of Brighton is one of the universities in the UK working with the University Studies Abroad Consortium which recruits students from all over the United States to study for one or two semesters in the UK. Students all study the British Culture module and then enrol on selected modules in faculties across the University. All of these are awarded credits transferable to their home university. Students also have the opportunity to participate in all of the field trips offered.

US Exchange Programme in Teacher Education - Allows undergraduate American students to exchange one semester of their study in the UK with a British student. The programme, which is tailor-made to each individual student's needs, can also be offered in free standing mode.

Enquiries: Mary Jones; mary.jones@brighton.ac.uk

■ **Junior Year Abroad**

The Junior Year Abroad Program, based in the Chelsea School, which specializes in Physical Education, Sports Science, Dance and Leisure Studies, offers a one or two semester British experience to undergraduate students from abroad. In all the areas on offer students are able to gain credits accepted by home universities. A wide selection of modules are available including a special field-trip based module which provides an opportunity to discover more about their British experience.

Enquiries: Paul McNaught-Davis; Head of The Chelsea School; p.mcnaught-davis@brighton.ac.uk

■ **School of Languages Short Courses**

The School of Languages organises a variety of short courses in the area of educational technology with focus on updating teachers' practical skills in the use of the Internet, ICT, Email, Interactive Multimedia and Video. The School has excellent facilities to support these courses.

Enquiries: Professor Brian Hill, Head of School of Languages; b.hill@brighton.ac.uk

Graduate School of Education   T: 0117 928 7048
8-10 Berkeley Square   F: 0117 922 5563
BRISTOL   BS8 1HH   E: jacqui.upcott@bristol.ac.uk
W: www.bristol.ac.uk/Depts/Education

MASTER'S DEGREES

■ MEd

Length of course: 12 months f/t; up to 5 years p/t
Entry requirements:
Graduates: An honours degree of a UK university or of CNAA; or, subject to Senate's approval, of any other university; or a Diploma in Advanced Studies in Education of the University of Bristol or its equivalent; at least one year's appropriate professional experience.
Non-graduates: A teaching or other appropriate professional qualification and at least one year appropriate professional experience. Non-graduates will be registered initially for the Advanced Diploma and may have their registration transferred to the MEd upon completion of four assignments at an appropriate standard (completed Diploma units will be counted towards the MEd).
Course content: The MEd degree consists of 180 credit points, ie 120 credit points of coursework and a further 60 credit points arising from the writing of a dissertation. Students choose either a Specialist Line of Study offered in
• Research Training
• Management & Policy Studies
• Special Education
• Counselling in Education
• Psychology of Education
• Education & Development
• Learning & Change
• Teaching English as a Foreign Language
• Mathematics Education
or an Individually Constructed Programme according to their special interests and objectives.

■ Professional Training Programme in Educational Psychology

■ MSc in Education, Technology and Society

■ MSc in Information and Library Management

■ PGDip/MSc in Counselling

RESEARCH DEGREES

■ MPhil, PhD

The Graduate School of Education has an international reputation for its research and an extremely strong research culture. It was the only Education Department in England to receive a top 5* grade in the 2001 Research Assessment Exercise. The specialist work of seven Research Centres contributes to an integrative theme of Culture and

Learning in Organisations (CLIO). This focuses our efforts on an issue of enormous significance for policy and practice in our complex and rapidly changing world. Research students join one of the Research Centres:

- Learners in Society
- Learning, Knowing & Interactive Technologies
- Psychology & Language Studies
- Assessment Studies
- Cultural, Management & Policy Studies
- International & Comparative Studies
- Counselling & Learning

The Graduate School of Education is recognised by ESRC for providing high quality research training. We will support the development of applications for ESRC studentships and expect there to be at least three University of Bristol studentships.

<u>Length of course:</u> *MPhil:* 1 year (min) f/t or 2 years of p/t study

PhD: 3 years (min) f/t or 6 years of p/t study

<u>Entry requirements:</u> Normally a good honours or a master's degree; applicants are asked in the first instance to send with their application an outline of the research they wish to undertake and to show the methods of study which they would use. Research students who do not hold a research master's degree are normally required to register for the degree of MPhil in the first instance; they may subsequently be upgraded to PhD candidature in the light of the progress they have made.

■ EdD Management

The Bristol course was the first doctoral programme in Education in Britain. It is now in its twelfth year and has had over 70 graduates. Participants include senior professionals from HE, FE, nurse education, psychological services, schools and LEAs and come from all parts of the UK, Europe and the world. The programme has an international reputation for its high quality and flexibility which includes:

- Teaching via intensive three day units
- Use of weekends and vacations
- Entry at any time
- Flexible pacing within a modular structure
- Continuous assessment
- Choice of dissertation topic

While continuing to draw on the Graduate School of Education's considerable expertise in Management and Administration of Education, the programme has been expanded to incorporate Culture and Learning in Organisations as a central theme. It provides excellent support for research and opportunities for publication.

The degree is also offered in Hong Kong in association with City University of Hong Kong (further information available at www.cityu.hk/ce/courses.html)

<u>Length of course:</u> 3 years (min) f/t; the programme can also be studies p/t

<u>Entry requirements:</u> Normally a UK degree or its equivalent; an advanced qualification in education; at least three years' appropriate professional experience.

<u>Course content/structure:</u> The programme consists of eight taught units (for students with a suitable master's degree; those who do not have such a degree take 12 units)

and a dissertation of not more than 40,000 words which represents a contribution to knowledge, showing evidence of originality, critical insight and the capacity to carry out independent research.

Taught units: (units are not necessarily offered every year)
- The Management & Leadership of Educational Organisations
- Education Policy
- Educational Assessment & Evaluation
- Human Resource Management in Education
- Learning in Organisations
- Adults & Professional Learning
- International Studies & the Management of Learning in Organisations
- Supervised Individual Study
- Management of Change
- Learning with New Technologies
- Changing Modes of Professionalism
- The Learning Organisation in Education
- Ethical Issues in Education
- Comparative Perspectives, Globalisation and Education
- Higher Education - Contemporary Policies, Cultures & Management
- Research Methods *(various units)*

The modular structure enables participants to organise their studies according to the time available and can be entered at any point during the year. The taught units are presented in intensive two and a half day blocks at the University. Participants fit their writing assignments, tutorials and library study into the periods between teaching blocks.

■ EdD Psychology

This new doctoral programme has been designed specifically to meet the continuing professional development needs of established and qualified Educational Psychologists who want to upgrade their qualifications to doctoral level. The programme is identical to the EdD Management *(see above)* except for including the following four compulsory units which cover significant research developments in educational psychology:
- Professional Supervision
- Professional Judgement & Decision-making
- Consultation in the Practice of Educational Psychology
- Research Issues in Educational Psychology

■ TESOL / Applied Linguistics

This new specialist pathway has been designed specifically to help English Language teaching professionals to update their knowledge and skills and to prepare themselves for new roles and functions as they develop their careers. The programme is identical to the EdD Management *(see above)* except for including the following four compusory units:

- Researching Language Classrooms
- Analysing Language
- Evaluation of Innovation and Programmes in English Language Education
- New Directions in Language Testing & Assessment

OTHER COURSES

■ **Study Attachment Programmes**
Length of courses: usually 1-6 months
These programmes are offered to individuals or to groups of up to 20 participants, particularly to senior educationalists who require an opportunity to extend their experience and competence through the study and first-hand observation in depth of a particular aspect of educational practice and for whom certification is unimportant. They are tailored to individual needs and normally include a planned programme of visits and attachments and a structured reading programme, coupled with tutorials or seminars. The outcome is usually a document of direct relevance to the participant's professional development.
In recent years study programmes have been developed in the following areas:
- Management of Initial and In-service Training of Teachers
- Organisation & Administration of LEAs
- School Inspection & Supervision
- Curriculum Development in Science & Maths
- Management of Schools & Colleges
- Organisation of Support Services for Teachers, including Resource & Teachers' Centres
- Resources for Learning & Classroom Management
- IT & Education
- Guidance & Counselling
- English as Medium of Instruction in the Teaching of Science & Maths
- Development of Training Programmes for Head Teachers & the 'Training of Trainers'
- Computer-assisted Language Learning
Fees: upon request (depending on length of course and numbers of participants)

FEES: £7500 pa for all award-bearing courses

ENQUIRIES: See contact details at beginning of entry.

Department of Education
Twickenham Campus
300 St Margaret's Road
TWICKENHAM TW1 1PT

T: 020 8891 0121
F: 020 8744 2960
E: school.education@brunel.ac.uk
W: www.brunel.ac.uk/faculty/ed

Head of Department: Professor Martin Cortazzi

The Department of Education has a strong national reputation for researching inclusive education, raising learners' attainment, developing philosophy for children and supporting gifted and talented pupils. The Department hosts the BFSS National Religious Education Centre, the Brunel Able Children's Education Centre, the Centre for Research in Teaching Thinking, the Centre for Youth Work Studies. A distinctive feature of students' experience of studying Education in this Department is that the process of learning is informed by cutting-edge research by staff in the three strands of: Critical Professional Education; Enhancing Learning and Teaching; Inclusive Education. The Department has a long tradition of innovation and excellence. We were the first in the field of teacher education in the UK. We are a leading department in developing new flexible routes into teaching. Our undergraduate courses have been rated as 'excellent' by OFSTED; our postgraduate courses have received 'excellent' ratings by OFSTED and the Quality Assurance Agency.

BACHELOR DEGREES

■ **BA Hons Primary Education** *(leading to a recommendation for QTS)*
This course prepares students to teach children within the Primary sector (ages 5-11) and has been developed in partnership with local schools and the Teacher Training Agency.
Length of course: 3 years
Entry requirements: GCE AS/GCE A-level/VCE A-level: 220-230 points, to include at least two subjects at GCE A-level/VCE 6-unit level, with one, preferably two, in National Curriculum subjects (English, Maths, any Science, ICT). Key Skills IT, Communication and Application of Number are normally required. Other qualifications - GCSE English and Maths at grade C or above, or their equivalent, are required to enter the teaching profession. Additionally, all new entrants born after 1 September 1979 must have the standard required to achieve grade C GCSE in a Science subject. Applications are also welcome from those with equivalent and non-standard qualifications. Your commitment to and suitability for entering the teaching profession will be discussed at interview.
Course content: This course focuses on the three core subjects within the primary National Curriculum - English, Maths, Science. Students develop one of these or ICT as their specialist subject. Shorter courses cover the remaining subjects: History, Music, PE, RE, Technology, Art, Geography. In the later stages of the course, students specialise in an age focus: 5-8 or 7-11. Wider issues relevant to primary teaching are addressed in Professional Education Studies: eg professional and legal responsibilities of teachers, personal tutoring and working with parents.
Assessment: Work will be assessed according to the level of study. Level 1 work (year 1) is classified as foundation level work, work at level 2 (year 2) and 3 (year 3) as the Honours part of the programme. The final year includes a major project. Levels 2 and 3

are weighted more heavily in the final degree classification.
Recommendation for QTS will be made to the Department for Education and Skills for all those who successfully demonstrate the Standards for QTS and pass the required National Basic Skills Tests.
Enquiries: T: 020 8891 0121, x2051

■ **BSc Hons Secondary Education and PE** *(leading to a recommendation for QTS)*
This course prepares students to teach children within the Secondary sector (ages 11-18) and has been developed in partnership with local schools and the Teacher Training Agency.
Length of course: 4 years
Entry requirements: GCE AS/GCE A-level/VCE A-level: 240-250 points, to include at least two subjects at GCE A-level/VCE 6-unit level, one at grade C or above, preferably in a Sports Studies or PE subject. Evidence of a good sporting profile will also be important. Key Skills IT, Communication and Application of Number are normally required. Other qualifications - GCSE English and Maths at grade C or above are required to enter the teaching profession. Applications are also welcome from those with equivalent and non-standard qualifications. Your commitment to and suitability for entering the teaching profession will be discussed at interview.
Course content: Two years' subject study are followed by two years' initial teacher education. Students undertake a variety of study tasks, including school-based and University-based work. The tasks are designed to enable students to link theory and practice, thought and action gained from their knowledge, understanding and application of secondary education.
Assessment: Work will be assessed according to the level of study. Level 1 work (year 1) is classified as foundation level work, work at levels 2 (years 2/3) and 3 (year 4) as the Honours part of the programme. The final year includes a major project. Levels 2 and 3 are weighted more heavily in the final degree classification.
Recommendation for QTS will be made to the Department for Education and Skills for all those who successfully demonstrate the Standards for QTS and pass the required National Basic Skills Tests.
Enquiries: T: 020 8891 0121, x2040

■ **BA Education Studies**
This new and dynamic course aims to provide an intellectually rigorous study of educational processes and the cultural, political and historical contexts in which they are embedded.
Length of course: 3 years
Entry requirements: GCE AS/GCE A-level/VCE A-level: 220-230 points, to include at least two subjects at GCE A-level/VCE 6-unit level. Key Skills IT, Communication and Application of Number are normally required. Other qualifications - GCSE in English, Maths and Science preferred. Non-standard qualifications from mature students, such as Access routes in leisure management and health studies will be considered. Applicants with a GNVQ merit/distinction profile will normally be considered.
Course content: Students undertake a variety of study tasks, including school-based and University-based work. The tasks are designed to enable students to link theory and practice, thought and action gained from the knowledge, understanding and application of secondary education.

Assessment: Work will be assessed according to the level of study. Level 1 work (year 1) is classified as foundation level work, work at level 2 (year 2) and level 3 (year 3) as the Honours part of the programme. The final year includes a major project. Levels 2 and 3 are weighed more heavily in the final degree classification.
Enquiries: T: 020 8891 0121, x2053.

Fees: (for all Bachelor degrees):
EU students: £1075
Non-EU students: *Non-laboratory subjects:* £7075
                          Laboratory subjects: £9400

CERTIFICATES / DIPLOMAS

■ **PGCE Primary** *(leading to a recommendation for QTS)*
Length of course: 1 year f/t
Entry requirements: Relevant first degree or equivalent; English and Maths, and Science for those born after 1979, at GCSE grade C standard or equivalent; previous study of chosen specialist subject to either A-level or in Higher Education.
Course content: This course gives a complete overview of the primary National Curriculum with particular emphasis on the three core subjects of English, Maths and Science, as well as ICT. One of these is developed as a specialism. Wider issues relevant to primary teaching are addressed in Professional Education Studies: eg professional and legal responsibilities of teachers, personal tutoring and working with parents. About 50% of the course takes place in schools: visits to a link school, serial school experience and two blocks of full-time school experience. Before commencing the University-based part of the course, students are required to arrange a week of structured observation in a primary school.
Assessment: Recommendation for QTS will be made to the Department for Education and Skills for all those who successfully demonstrate the Standards for QTS and pass the required National Basic Skills Tests.
Enquiries: T: 020 8891 0121, x2051

■ **PGCE Secondary** *(leading to a recommendation for QTS)*
Length of course:
1 year f/t for: English, ICT, Maths, MFL, PE, RE, Science.
11 weeks (min) - 2 years (max) by distance learning for: Biology, Physics, Chemistry, English, Maths (these TTA-approved courses will provide individual training plans and flexible course provision according to qualifications and experience).
Entry requirements: Relevant first degree or equivalent; English and Maths at GCSE grade C standard or equivalent.
Course content: This course consists of three main types of experience:
• *Education Studies* which focus on issues of common interest to all secondary school teachers:
  • Special education needs, including needs of the most able
  • Assessment and its role in promoting learning
  • Whole-school policies
  • Equal opportunities
  • English as an additional language

- Teachers' legal responsibilities
- Professional learning
- *Subject Studies* give a firm grounding in all National Curriculum subjects and enable students to teach across the 11-18 age range. Particular focus is on the subject specialism, including an introduction to curriculum organisation, methods of working and safety and use of ICT in teaching the specialism.
- *Serial and block teaching experience in two different schools* - at least two-thirds of the course is school-based, in line with the DfES requirements. The Department works in a consortium of four Higher Education establishments for the purpose of school placements.

Assessment: Recommendation for QTS will be made to the Department for Education and Skills for all those who successfully demonstrate the Standards for QTS and pass the required National Basic Skills Tests.

Fees: EU students: £1075
     Non-EU students: Non-laboratory subjects: £7075
                      Laboratory subjects: £9400

Enquiries: T: 020 8891 0121, x2040

MASTER'S DEGREES / CERTIFICATES / DIPLOMAS

- **MA / Postgraduate Diploma / Postgraduate Certificate in**
  Education
  Primary Education
  Secondary Education
  Special Educational Needs
  Guidance & Counselling Skills
  Information Technology in Education
  Educational Management

Length of course: 1 year f/t; 2 years p/t

Entry requirements: A British honours degree or other qualification considered by the university to be an acceptable alternative; professional experience in teaching, training or work in a related profession.

Assessment: By a 4000-word assignment per module, plus a final 15,000-word dissertation.

Fees: EU students: £2805 pa f/t; £175 per module p/t
     Non-EU students: £7075 pa f/t; £575 per module p/t

Enquiries: T: 020 8891 0121, x2051

MASTER'S DEGREES

- **MA Youth & Community Studies**

Length of course: 2/3 years distance learning

Entry requirements: A British honours degree or other qualification considered by the university to be an acceptable alternative; two years' professional experience in Youth and Community work teaching, training or work in a related profession.

Assessment: On a continuous basis throughout the course, including module assignments and a dissertation.

Fees: Home-based (member organisations): £1645 pa
    Non-member: £1845 pa
    Ireland Programme: £1650 pa
    Overseas fee: £3980 pa
Enquiries: T: 020 8891 0121, x2039

RESEARCH DEGREES

■ **MPhil, PhD, EdD**

Length of course: *MPhil:* 12 months f/t; 24 months p/t
                   PhD: 36 months f/t; 48 months p/t
                   EdD: 36 months f/t; 48 months p/t *(may be reduced for applicants with an appropriate Masters Degree)*

Entry requirements: *PhD:* normally restricted to candidates holding a higher research degree.
                       EdD: normally a Masters Degree and 4 years professional experience.

It is possible to regrade from MPhil to PhD where satisfactory progress has been made after an initial period of study.

Course content: The work of research students in the preparation of a thesis for these degrees is supervised by two University tutors. All students are expected to complete a programme of research training. The EdD, which is a professional doctorate, requires attendance at assessed taught courses and completion of an Institution Focused Study (10,000 words) and a thesis (30,000 words).

Fees: *MPhil/PhD:* EU students: £2805 f/t; £1830 p/t
                   Non-EU students: £7075 f/t; £4260 p/t
      EdD: EU students: £350 per module
                   Non-EU students: £5660
Enquiries: T: 020 8891 0121, x2409/2053

OTHER COURSES

The Short Courses Office runs a large number of events throughout the year, mainly in the fields of Science and Technology. These range from one-day workshops and conferences to three/four-day accredited courses for safety certification one- and two-week foundation and up-dating courses in Science and Technology and individual modules which can carry credit towards a Masters award.

There are no formal entry requirements for most short courses, but since they are designed for secondary school teachers the majority of participants are qualified teachers. Most courses offer the opportunity for subject up-dating in the context of the English education system.

The Short Courses Office is also responsible for providing advice for Overseas Trained Teachers (OTTs) who have teaching posts in English schools (Primary and Secondary) and who wish to gain English Qualified Teacher Status (QTS) (candidates must be employed in a school prior to seeking QTS).

Fees: £100 per day (average)
Enquiries: T: 020 8891 8278

UNIVERSITY OF CAMBRIDGE

Faculty of Education
a) 17 Trumpington Street
    CAMBRIDGE CB2 1QA
b) Shaftesbury Road
    CAMBRIDGE CB2 2BX
c) Hills Road
    CAMBRIDGE CB2 2PH

T: 01223 332888
F: 01223 332894
T: 01223 369631
F: 01223 324421
T: 01223 507222
F: 01223 507120

E: educ-inst-tutorial@lists.cam.ac.uk
W: www.educ.cam.ac.uk

Head of School: Professor Donald McIntyre
Enquiries: The Secretary of the Faculty

BACHELOR DEGREES

■ **BA in Education Studies**
Length of course: 3 years
Course content: This course offers the opportunity to combine the academic study of the main disciplines of education (history, philosophy, psychology and sociology) with study in another subject selected from the following:
• Biological Science
• English (with Drama option)
• Geography
• History
• Maths
• Music
• Religious Studies
The course prepares students for a variety of possible careers in Education and related fields and provides a good foundation for those wishing to continue on to the PGCE and QTS. It is also open to graduates of other universities entering as Affiliated Students.
Enquiries: Trumpington Street or Hills Road (contact details above)
Fees: Tuition: EU students: £1075
                 Non-EU students: £7248
      College: £2500 (average)

MASTER'S DEGREES

■ **MPhil, MEd**
Length of courses: MPhil: 1 year f/t
                    MEd: 2 years p/t
Entry requirements: Applicants should normally be honours graduates, though comparable qualifications in other areas may be accepted. Additionally, applicants for the MEd degree will be expected to have a minimum of three years' teaching experience.
Course content: Both degrees offer graduate students, teachers, advisors and other persons professionally involved in education, whether from Britain or from overseas, the opportunity to pursue advanced study in education, familiarise themselves with

Glossary on page XI

educational research, policy and practice and to extend their professional knowledge and skills. Both courses have a strong research focus and cater for a range of specialist and/or generalist interests with the flexibility for individual students to plan, with academic advice, a course to meet personal priorities.

Assessment: through submitted work

Fees: MPhil: Tuition: EU students: £2805
Non-EU students: £7248
College: £2500 (average)

MEd: Tuition: EU students: £1402 pa
Non-EU students: £3624 pa
College: £300-£400 (average)

Enquiries: MPhil: Trumpington Street (contact details see beginning of entry)
MEd: Shaftesbury Road (contact details see beginning of entry)

CERTIFICATES / DIPLOMAS

■ **Advanced Diploma in Educational Studies**
Length of course: 1 year f/t
Course content: A programme may be constructed from a selection of modules designed for qualified teachers working in primary, secondary or further education. There are also specialist courses in the Education of Children with Special Educational Needs.
Enquiries: Shaftesbury Road (contact details see beginning of entry)

■ **PGCE Primary and Secondary**
Length of course: 1 year f/t
Entry requirements: A British honours degree in subject specialism chosen or recognised equivalent.
Course content: Students train to teach in British schools at either Primary (4-8 years or 7-11 years) or Secondary (11-18 years) level. For Secondary training, students specialise in one of the following subjects:
• Biology, Chemistry or Physics (all with Combined Science)
• Classics
• English
• Geography
• History
• Maths
• Modern Languages (one of which must be French)
• Religious Studies
Enquiries: Hills Road (contact details see beginning of entry)

RESEARCH DEGREES

■ MPhil, MSc, MLitt, PhD

All research degrees require full-time study under supervision within the University. Supervision is available for work related to any level or form of education: nursery, primary, secondary, special, tertiary, university and professional.

Length of course: MPhil: 1 year
                  MSc/MLitt: 2 years
                  PhD: 3 years

Enquiries: Trumpington Street *(contact details see beginning of entry)*
Fees: *as for the MPhil degree - see Master's Degrees*

OTHER COURSES

■ Short Courses

A range of short courses designed to update current theory and practice and to develop skills in particular areas is offered to experienced teachers and other educationalists.

Length of courses: 1-10 days throughout the year
Enquiries: Shaftesbury Road *(contact details see beginning of entry)*

■ Individual Study Attachments

Individual study programmes may also be negotiated for those wishing to undertake supervised research into specific educational issues through our Schoolteacher Fellowship and Research Associateship schemes. Expertise is available to support a wide range of topics.

Length of course: *Schoolteacher Fellowship Scheme:* 1 term
                  Research Associateship Scheme: 1 year
Fees: EU students: £935 per term
      Non-EU students: £2416 per term
Enquiries: Shaftesbury Road *(contact details see beginning of entry)*

Canterbury Christ Church University College
CANTERBURY   CT1 1QU

T: 01227 782236 / 782991
F: 01227 785761
E: s.blandford@cant.ac.uk
W: www.cant.ac.uk

BACHELOR DEGREES

■ BA in Primary Education (age range 3-7/5-11)

<u>Length of course:</u> 3-4 years
Completion of the requirements of the 3-year course at an appropriate level leads to the award of a Honours Degree in addition to recommendation for QTS.
<u>Entry requirements:</u> GCSE A-C English, Maths, Science or equivalent; 2 A-levels at grade C or above or equivalent.
<u>Course content:</u>
• Subject studies
• Professional studies
• Serial and block placements
<u>Assessment:</u> Coursework, examinations, portfolios.
<u>Fees:</u> EU students: £1025
       Non-EU students: £5700

■ BA Hons (Joint/Combined) Early Childhood Studies

<u>Length of course:</u> 3 years f/t
<u>Entry requirements:</u> 2 A-levels at grade C or above or equivalent.
<u>Course content:</u>
• Development Psychology
• Anthropology
• History
• Sociology
• Law
• Young Children with Special Needs
<u>Assessment:</u> Coursework (75%), examinations (25%).
<u>Fees:</u> EU students: £1025
       Non-EU students: £5700

■ BA Hons Professional Studies (Post-compulsory Education & Training)

This is an in-service course for teachers and trainers and can be specifically adapted to meet the needs of particular institutions and public/private sector organisations.
<u>Length of course:</u> 2 years p/t
<u>Entry requirements:</u> Certificate of Education
<u>Course content:</u> Four units:
• Analysis of Curriculum Issue
• Studies in Curriculum Development
• Action Research in Teaching
• Curriculum Project
<u>Fees:</u> EU students: £1500
       Non-EU students: £6000

CERTIFICATES / DIPLOMAS

■ PGCE Primary (age range 3-7/5-11)
Length of course: 1 year f/t; 5 terms p/t, modular
Entry requirements: Relevant first degree; GCSE in English, Maths, Science.
Course content: College-based courses in:
- Subject studies
- Professional studies
- Serial and block school placements

Assessment: Student teachers must pass both college- and school-based elements of the course.
Fees: EU students: £2675
      Non-EU students: £6546

■ PGCE Key Stage 2/3 (age range 7-14)
Length of course: 1 year f/t; modular programme available in Music
Entry requirements: Relevant first degree; GCSE in English and Maths (and Science if born on or after 1 Sept. 1979).
Course content: Subjects available:
- English
- French
- Geography
- Maths
- Music
- RE
- Science

Assessment: Student teachers must pass both college- and school-based elements of the course.
Fees: EU students: £2675
      Non-EU students: £6000

■ PGCE Secondary (age range 11-18)
Length of course: 1 year f/t; modular programme available in Secondary English, Maths, Music.
Entry requirements: Relevant first degree; GCSE in English and Maths
Course content: Secondary subjects available:
- Art
- Citizenship
- English
- Geography
- History
- ICT
- Maths
- MFL
- Music
- PE
- RE
- Science

Other details as PGCE Primary above. There may be opportunity to complete part of the course in Europe.

■ **PGCE / Maîtrise FLE with Université du Littoral, Côte Opale**
Length of course: 11 months
Entry requirements: First degree or equivalent.
Course content: College-based courses in:
• Subject Studies
• Pedagogy and General Professional Studies
• Language Teaching Methodology
• 2 school placements
• A 4-month period in France on a Maîtrise FLE course at the Université du Littoral, Côte Opale
A key joint focus is on ICT in MFL teaching and learning.
Assessment: Student teachers must pass both college- and school-based elements of the course.
Fees: EU students: no fees
      Non-EU students: £6000

■ **PGCE (Post-compulsory)**
Length of course: 1 year f/t
Entry requirements: Relevant first degree; experience.
Course content: College-based curriculum studies; specialist studies in one of the following areas:
• Business Administration
• Sport, Leisure & Tourism
• Humanities & Social Sciences
• Science, Maths & Technology
• Health & Care
There are two teaching placements in partner colleges.
Fees: EU students: £1025
      Non-EU students: £6000

■ **PGCE / Advanced Certificate in Education (Post-compulsory)**
This is an in-service course for teachers and trainers and can be specifically adapted to meet the needs of particular institutions and public/private sector organisations. This award is recognised by FENTO.
Length of course: 2 years p/t
Entry requirements: Relevant first degree or equivalent.
Course content:
• Theories of Learning
• Curriculum Organisation & Development
• Policy Development & Philosophical Issues
• Management & Delivery of Learning
• Assessment & Evaluation
• Self-Evaluation
• Professional Role

There is a period of supervised teaching practice. A dissertation at level M must be completed.

Fees: EU students: £510
Non-EU students: £6000

MASTER'S DEGREES

- **MA Educational Studies**
- **MA Enabling Learning**
- **MA Lifelong Learning**
- **MA Literacy**
- **MA Management Studies**
- **MA Post-Compulsory Education & Training**
- **MA Subject Leadership**

Modular postgraduate diploma. Flexible programme offering a wide variety of modules, each of one term's duration. Candidates must accumulate 180 credits.

Length of course: 2-4 years

Entry requirements: Honours degree 2.2 or above or its equivalent and related professional experience.

Course content: Six modules in individually chosen areas; dissertation.

Assessment: Each module will culminate in an assignment to the value of 4000 words or equivalent.

Fees: £6200

RESEARCH DEGREES

- **MPhil/PhD**

These degrees are based on the individual pursuit of a research project.

Entry requirements: At least a good second class honours degree; all applicants are considered on an individual basis and holders of other qualifications are welcome to apply.

Assessment: A thesis which embodies the result of research undertaken during the period of registration. MPhil candidates are required to demonstrate an appropriate ability to conduct an original investigation, to test ideas and to understand the relationship of the topic or theme investigated to a wider field of knowledge.

Fees: £6200

Cardiff School of Social Sciences
Glamorgan Building
King Edward VII Avenue
CARDIFF CF10 3WT

T: 029 2087 5179
F: 029 20874175
E: *Undergraduate:* socsi-ug@cf.ac.uk
Postgraduate: socsi-pg@cf.ac.uk
W: www.cf.ac.uk/socsi

<u>Director of School:</u> Professor Huw Beynon

The Cardiff School of Social Sciences is part of Cardiff University, a constituent college of the University of Wales. The School caters for national and international students. During the last decade it has attracted students from over 75 countries. Many of the staff continue to consult with the educational services of overseas countries whilst arranging a variety of courses to meet national and international needs.
Cardiff is the capital city of Wales and has many attractions for international students. English and Welsh are the two official languages, although English is used for the majority of teaching. Cardiff is two hours from London by rail and it has its own international airport. The city has a cosmopolitan nature and has an exciting range of cultural and sporting amenities.
Cardiff University has a strong profile in the field of education. For example, during the last five years alone we have attracted over £2.500,000 in external funding for educational research from the Economic Social Research Council (ESRC), major national charities and other funding bodies. In the past, educational courses and researchers at Cardiff were dispersed across more than one department. The creation of the new School of Social Sciences has now brought them together to work on a broad range of educational issues.

Educational teaching and research at Cardiff has the following **distinctive features**:

- *Education is a lifelong process* - We see learning as taking place in a variety of social contexts; in schools, colleges and universities certainly, but also within families, work-places and wider community settings.
- *Education can not be divorced from society* - We believe that educational change needs to be understood in relation to other elements of the social structure, such as families, labour markets and political and cultural institutions. We are committed to taking a leading role in the new generation of educational research, which explores the relationship between processes of learning and other dimensions of individual and social life.
- *Educational research needs an inter-disciplinary, social scientific framework* - A key aim of the new School is to foster high quality, inter-disciplinary social scientific research and this aim provides an important context for our educational research. An inter-disciplinary approach, we believe, is vital for theory-building, and for the development of policy and professional practice.
- *Educational research needs high quality methodologies* - Developing, applying and providing training in rigorous research methodologies is central to the School's mission and colleagues working within the field of education have international reputations for their developmental work in both qualitative and quantitative methodologies.

Within the School of Sciences there are two closely related **research groups** focusing explicitly on educational issues:

• The *'Culture Learning and Society' group (ClaS)*
This group has an extensive programme of research projects, for the most part funded by the ESRC and charitable foundations. It is currently strategically focused in four areas:

- organisational change and organisational learning in schools
- the social impacts of changes in educational policy
- the determinants of school attainment
- methodological development and training

Recent major research grants have funded work on: patterns of participation in life long learning; the role of technology in widening participation in life long learning; measuring markets in the public sector; changes in public sector higher education; children's use of new technologies in the home; the comparative performance of boys and girls at school in Wales; the future role of higher education within teacher education and training. In addition the group is also the location for the ESRC 'Teaching and Learning Research Capability-building Network' providing methodological support and training for educational researchers across the UK.

• The *'Applied Social and Developmental Psychology' group (ASDeP)*
This is a well-established Research Group in an area where Cardiff has a substantial tradition of high-quality research. In recent years, Group members have been very successful in developing major research projects, funded by the ESRC and government departments and agencies. The Group's research programme has embodied two principal themes:

- learning and its determinants
- social psychological aspects of children and education

Each of these involves the application of theory and methodologies from developmental, social and cognitive psychology to educational and other learning settings. Recent major research grants have funded work on: shyness, pre-school education, educational provision for traveller children, early literacy development.

In addition, many other of the School's research groups in health and criminology have a broadly educational dimension to their work.

The following course programmes of study are popular and are of interest to overseas students. Special programmes can be arranged to meet the specific requirements of students and visiting academics from overseas to fit in with particular development plans if required.

BACHELOR DEGREES

■ **BA in Education**
Length of course: 3 years f/t
Entry requirements: 3 A-levels or equivalent.
Course content:
Part 1: Modules in Education and Educational Psychology, plus two additional subjects offered within the Faculty of Humanities and Social Studies.

Part 2: The BA Modular Scheme provides for programmes of study which emphasise either psychology curriculum or policy and sociology. Joint degree schemes allow for programmes of study with increased credits in other subjects.
<u>Fees:</u> EU students: £1075
        Non-EU students: £7200
<u>Enquiries:</u> Joanna Wilkes; wilkesjk@cf.ac.uk

■ **BEd (Vocational Training)**
<u>Length of course:</u> 2 years p/t
<u>Entry requirements:</u> The course provides a route to graduate status for educators/trainers working with the 16+ age group. Candidates should be in possession of one of the following:
• A non-graduate Teacher's Certificate awarded by an approved university or the CNAA
• City and Guilds revised 730 Award
• NCVQ Level Three Trainer/Assessor Award
• City and Guilds Training Award 7254
• Diploma in Youth Work or Community Education awarded by an approved university or the CNAA
• Other qualifications or experience deemed equivalent by the Board of Studies
<u>Course content:</u> After an initial bridging course in vocational training and mentoring skills students follow a variety of modules including:
• Teaching and learning processes and strategies
• Research techniques
• Training in organisations
• Management skills and concepts
• Curriculum development
In addition all students are required to complete a research project of approximately 8,000 words.
<u>Fees:</u> Bridging Course £250, then £530 pa
<u>Enquiries:</u> Susan Hayes; hayessm@cf.ac.uk

MASTER'S DEGREES

■ **MA in Education**
<u>Length of course:</u> 1 year (min) f/t; 2-5 years (min) p/t
<u>Entry requirements:</u> First degree or equivalent; teaching qualification and two years' qualified professional experience.
<u>Course content/structure:</u> Students must complete six modules and a 20,000-word (max) dissertation. A Diploma will be awarded to students who are successful in their course work.
In most cases modules are free-standing with no prerequisites. In certain cases, however, a prerequisite *core* module may be required before the related *elective* module may be taken. The following modules are offered either on a taught or supported study basis:

- Behaviour Problems
- Child Development
- Globalisation & Education
- Leadership & Management in Educational Organisations
- TEFL I: Fundamental Issues in Language Teaching
- TEFL II: Applied Linguistics
- *Dissertation Preparation*
- *Two modules from other Master's courses in the School of Social Sciences may be taken*

Fees: EU students: £2805 f/t
£468 per 20-credit module; £234 per 10-credit module
Non-EU students: £7200 f/t
Enquiries: Anna Brown; browna1@cf.ac.uk

CERTIFICATES / DIPLOMAS

- **PGCE** (Further Education)
- **Certificate in Education** (Further Education)
- **Teacher's Certificate** (Overseas)

Length of course: 36 weeks f/t; 16 months p/t (a 1-week block followed by day release - one day per week - for 36 weeks)

Entry requirements: The course is open to those who are qualified in their teaching subject and wish to teach in the further education sector which includes technical colleges, nurse and paramedical training establishments as well as serving technical teachers who are professionally qualified in their subject area and who wish to be professionally trained as teachers.

Course content: The course consists of theoretical and practical components supported by regular and frequent individual and group tutorials, together with course work assignments.

Fees: EU students: £1075 f/t
Non-EU students: £7200 f/t
Enquiries: Heather Easen; easenhl@cf.ac.uk

RESEARCH DEGREES

- **MPhil, PhD**

Length of course: *MPhil:* 1 year f/t; 2 years p/t (min)
PhD: 3 years f/t; 3 years p/t (min)

Entry requirements: As a minimum a good honours degree (BA, BSc, BEd) or equivalent qualification. Places are offered on the basis of the applicant's qualifications, the strength of the research proposal and the School of Social Science's ability to provide appropriate supervision. Applicants are urged to pay particular attention to submitting a detailed research proposal with their application form. All overseas students must show evidence of proficiency in written and spoken English and may be required to attend English language classes during their studies if necessary. PhD applicants may be accepted for a 1- to 2-year probationary period unless they are holders of an approved Masters degree. Students will normally be expected to follow programmes in research methods.

Research areas:
The School welcomes applications from students interested in researching a wide range of educational issues including:
- Educational Policy & Schooling
- Human Development & Learning
- Learning, Work & Labour Markets
- Young People, Education & Disadvantage
- Sociology of Science & Expertise

Other areas of social science where the School offers supervision include:
- Crime, Risk & Governance
- Health, Welfare & Risk
- Industrial & Social Change
- Theory, Environment & Public Policy
- Wales, Policy & Devolution

Assessment: A written thesis and an oral examination.
Fees: EU students: £2805 f/t; £1402 p/t
      Non-EU students: £7200
Enquiries: Elizabeth Renton; renton@cf.ac.uk

■ EdD

Length of course: 3 years
Entry requirements: An advanced qualification in the field of Education; at least three years' appropriate professional experience.
Course content: 24 modules - 12 form the taught portion of the programme, 12 are represented by the production of a research thesis. Six of the taught modules are concerned with aspects of education management, two with education policy formation and the remaining four are devoted to research practices.
Fees: EU students: £2336 pa; £292 per module
      Non-EU students: £7200 pa
Enquiries: Elizabeth Renton; renton@cf.ac.uk

OTHER COURSES

■ Special Courses and Attachments at Post- and Pre-doctoral Level

In addition to the established courses, group courses can be arranged at special request by overseas students. Some examples of such courses are:
- Adult Education
- Educational Technology
- School Management & Improvement
- Distance Learning
- Organisation & Planning of Primary/Secondary/Tertiary Educational Institutions
- Special Education Needs
- Subject Leadership in Schools
- Headteacher Assessment & Training

UNIVERSITY OF CENTRAL ENGLAND

Faculty of Education   T: 0121 331 7300
Perry Barr   F: 0121 331 7316
BIRMINGHAM   B42 2SU   W: www.uce.ac.uk

Dean of the Faculty of Education: Professor Roger Woods
Contact person: Dr Janet Hoskyns; janet.hoskyns@uce.ac.uk; T: 0121 331 7337

BACHELOR DEGREES

■ **BA Hons Primary Education with QTS**
Length of course: 4 years f/t
Entry requirements: Standard university entry requirements and additional DfES re-
quirements for teacher training; GCSE Grade C or equivalent in English Language,
Maths and a Science subject and an appropriate background for the chosen specialist
subject; relevant experience with children, preferably in mainstream primary schools.
Course content/structure: The course requires full-time attendance. Study is divided
between teaching studies, specialist subject study and school-based work.
Assessment: There is a combination of examinations, assessed coursework and teaching practice in all years which cumulatively contributes towards meeting the DfES
standards for newly qualified teachers.
Fees: on application
Enquiries: Marion Harris; T: 0121 331 7300; E: janet.hill@uce.ac.uk

■ **BA Hons Early Childhood Education Studies**
This course provides a progression route to degree level for students with an HND
related to the early years (0-8). It aims to develop confident and articulate practitioners
in early childhood education.
Length of course: 1 years f/t; 2 years p/t
Entry requirements: An HND in Early Childhood Studies (completed or about to be
completed).
Course content/structure:
Students study four core compulsory modules:
• Research and Dissertation
• Policy and Practice - Inclusion and Equal Opportunities
• Perceptions of Childhood
• Play and Exploration
Modules include taught sessions, presentations, workshops, independent study and
research.
Assessment: A research-based dissertation; essays and reports; presentations and
supporting evidence.
Enquiries: Sarah Marshall; sarah.marshall@uce.ac.uk

CERTIFICATES / DIPLOMAS

■ PGCE Secondary Education (Drama or Music)

Length of course: 1 year f/t

Entry requirements: A degree or acceptable equivalent qualification; GCSE at grade C or above or equivalent in English Language and Maths.

Enquiries: Simon Spencer; T: 0121 331 7356/7315; E: janet.hill@uce.ac.uk

■ PGCE Primary Education (5-11)

Length of course: 1 year f/t

Entry requirements: A degree or equivalent qualification recognised by the DfES and an education providing the necessary foundation for work as a primary school teacher; GCSE at grade C or above or equivalent in English Language and Maths. Applicants who were born on or after 1 September 1979 will be required to have attained GCSE grade C in Science or science subject(s).

Fees: on application

Enquiries: Lynn Fulford; T: 0121 331 7320/7315; E: janet.hill@uce.ac.uk

■ Certificate of Higher Education: Further Education

This course is designed for practising teachers and trainers working with learners aged 16+. It provides a course of training to meet FENTO standards for existing p/t and fractional teachers in Further Education who are not graduates.

Length of course: 1 year f/t; 2 years p/t

Entry requirements: English and Maths at GCSE grade C or equivalent; access to 120 hours teaching in Further Education. Applicants with the City & Guilds 730 Further & Adult Education Teachers' Certificate will be able to enrol in Year Two.

Course content/structure:

YEAR ONE consists of two stages:

Stage One consists of two modules, each with an assignment of 1500 words:
• Lesson Planning
• Learning Resources

Stage Two consists of three modules, each with an assignment:
• Action Learning and Study Skills
• Assessment and Evaluation
• Observation and Teaching File

YEAR TWO consists of five modules:
• Teaching & Learning
• The Practice of Teaching
• 16+ Curriculum in Context
• Effective Strategies for Adult Learning
• Staff Training & Development (half module)
• Effective Communication (half module)

Each module is assessed by an assignment of ca 2500 words or its equivalent.

Assessment: Assignments and teaching practice are assessed against FENTO standards.

Enquiries: Glynis Worrow; E: janet.hill@uce.ac.uk; T: 0121 331 7342/7315

CERTIFICATES / DIPLOMAS / MASTER'S DEGREES

■ PG Cert / PG Dip / MA Drama in Education

Length of course: 3 years p/t by Summer Schools
Entry requirements: First degree or equivalent or professional experience and experience of Drama.
Course content: A programme of advanced professional development for all those who have responsibility for using drama in any sort of teaching/learning context.
Assessment: By submission of coursework and a dissertation.
Fees: on application
Enquiries: MA Administrator; E: kerri.law@uce.ac.uk; T: 0121 331 7330

■ PG Cert / PG Dip / MA Education

Length of course: 3-6 (max) years p/t
Entry requirements: A good honours degree, a University Diploma and/or work experience in an appropriate setting are desirable. All applicants will be interviewed.
Fees: on application
Enquiries: MA Administrator; E: kerri.law@uce.ac.uk; T: 0121 331 7330

RESEARCH DEGREES

■ MPhil/PhD

Length of course: 3-5 years p/t; p/t overseas students are expected to study at the University for 6 weeks f/t in each year.
Entry requirements: A first or second class honours degree or equivalent. However, for those who do not have the standard entry qualifications, evidence of ability and relevant background knowledge, for example publications and academic references, may be taken into account.
Research areas: Design & Technology in Education, Drama in Education, Equal Opportunities in Education, Lifelong Learning, Maths Education, Music in Education, Science Education, School Effectiveness and Improvement, Management in Education and others.
Enquiries: Miriam Bartlett, Research Administrator; miriam.bartlett@uce.ac.uk; T: 0121 331 7334
Fees: EU students: £610 p/t
        Non-EU students: £6600 f/t; 1432 p/t

Department of Education & Social Science
Livesey House
PRESTON
PR1 2HE
T: 01772 893090/1/2/4
F: 01772 892922
E: kmphillips@uclan.ac.uk
W: www.uclan.ac.uk
Head of Department: Ken Phillips
Enquiries: T: 01772 893109 or 393090; gheywood-everett@uclan.ac.uk

The Department of Education & Social Science was established in 1995 in response to the innovative developments in the areas of
- Deaf Studies
- Education Studies
- Teaching and Training Studies

The Department is concerned with the critical examination of education in all its aspects, including:
- the advancement of theoretical understanding
- the relationship between theory and practice in educational and related contexts
- the political and social determinants of educational success

Members of the department have a particular interest in facilitating access for disadvantaged students, particularly deaf students. This is reflected in admissions policy as well as in the context of the curriculum and teaching philosophy. This provision was awarded the maximum points during a recent review by the Quality Assurance Agency. The assessors highlighted many strengths, including excellent learning and academic advice and the high level of achievement amongs non-traditional students.

BACHELOR DEGREES

■ BA Hons Teaching & Training Studies
Length of course: 2-5 years p/t
Entry qualifications: 2 A-levels or equivalent.
Course description: This course is designed primarily for serving teachers or trainers from the public or private sectors who do not have graduate status. The programme is based largely on practice where concepts and theories will be considered within the actual classroom context. There are four mandatory modules plus a dissertation; the remaining twelve optional modules may be chosen from an extensive list which includes:
- Studies in Management
- Mentoring
- Special Needs
- Professional Development

The modules are available at several centres both during the day and in the evening. Directed study modules which do not require attendance are also available. Teachers may be granted exemptions on the basis of previous experience and/or qualifications.
Assessment: Coursework and a dissertation.
Fees: £140 per module

MASTER'S DEGREES

■ MA Education (Leadership)

Length of course: 1 year f/t; 2 years p/t
Entry qualifications: Degree or equivalent.
Course description: Designed for education managers from schools, colleges or other educational institutions, this pathway is concerned with developing an understanding of and enthusiasm for educational leadership. There are three mandatory core modules, three optional modules and a dissertation. The core modules involve a study of strategic leadership and effective organisations and candidates are encouraged to develop change projects in the context of their own institutions. The three optional modules may be selected from a wide choice including Management, Education Studies and Special Educational Needs.
Assessment: Coursework and a dissertation.
Fees: £230 per module

■ MA Education (Research)

Length of course: 1 year f/t; 2 years p/t
Entry qualifications: Degree or equivalent.
Course description: This programme has been designed for practitioners in education or training who intend to undertake small-scale research within their own place of work. There are three mandatory core modules, three optional modules and a dissertation. The core modules involve a study of educational research methodology. The three optional modules may be selected from a wide choice including management, education studies and special educational needs.
Assessment: Coursework and a dissertation.
Fees: £230 per module

Other pathways focusing on Teaching and Training and Special Needs may be available 2002/03. Enquiries about these pathways and also about on-line learning should be addressed to the Departmental Administrator.

Chester College T: 01244 375444
Parkgate Road F: 01244 392820
CHESTER CH1 4BJ E: int.reg@chester.ac.uk
 W: www.chester.ac.uk

Dean of School of Education: Dr Elaine Barnes
Enquiries: int.reg@chester.ac.uk
Prospectus: The International Desk, Registry Services *(address see above)*

Programmes in Education have been offered at Chester College since 1839, when it was founded as the first Teacher Training College in the UK. The School of Education is now one of four Schools in the College - the others are Arts & Humanities, Science & Health and Nursing & Midwifery. The College offers degree study (undergraduate, postgraduate taught and research), awarded by the University of Liverpool. At *under-graduate* level, Education Studies are available as part of a Combined Subjects Honours degree, or students may take a four-year BEd Honours degree, specialising in Primary Education. PGCE is offered at Primary and Secondary levels. Continuing Professional Development opportunities are available at *postgraduate* level (Certificate or Diploma in Advanced Studies or Master of Education), and students are also able to register for MPhil or PhD research study.

BACHELOR DEGREES

■ BEd Hons with QTS
Length of course: 4 years f/t
Entry requirements: GCSE English Language, Maths and (for entrants under 21 years) Science, grade C or above. 14 points at A-level, including a grade C in the chosen specialist subject (currently PE, RE, Early Years, English with Drama). Experience within a primary school is also essential. *Applicants with other qualifications, please contact the Registry.*
Course content:
• School experience
• Professional development education
• Core subjects (English, Maths, Science)
• ICT
• Foundation Subjects
• RE
• Specialist subjects (currently available: English with Drama, RE, Early Years & PE, Sports Science)
Assessment: continuous

■ BA (Combined Subjects)
Length of course: 3 years f/t
Entry requirements: 14 points at A-level, including a grade C in one subject.
Course content: Education Studies is available as a minor or equal component of a joint Honours programme to students taking Art, Biology, Geography, History, Maths

or Theology & Religious Studies. Modules in Education Studies are available at each of the three levels of study.

Assessment: continuous

■ **PGCE Primary and Secondary**

Length of course: 1 year f/t (Secondary 36 weeks, Primary 38 weeks)

Entry requirements: A good honours degree (2.1 or above) in subjects directly related to the curriculum area, plus GCSE grade C or above in English Language, Maths and (for Primary applicants) a Science.

Course content: *Primary:* Specialism in English, Maths or Science; *Secondary:* Specialism in one of the following: Art, Drama, Maths, MFL (French, German or Spanish), PE, RE.

Assessment: continuous

Fees for BEd, BA, PGCE: EU students: £1050 pa
                  Non-EU students: £6540 pa

MASTER'S DEGREES / CERTIFICATES / DIPLOMAS

■ **MEd, Diploma, Certificate in Advanced Studies**

Length of course: Taught modules and supervised research are offered, which can be accumulated over a six-year period, according to the level of award. Study can also be taken on a full-time basis, with a one-year minimum time frame for completion of modules leading to a qualification.

Entry requirements: The modular programme is open to graduates and non-graduates with appropriate professional experience.

Course content: New programmes and modules are continually being designed to meet the needs of individuals and schools within the context of local and national priorities. For example, current areas of study cover: Curriculum English, ICT, Mathematical Education & Maths, School Management, School Improvement, Special Needs, Religious & Theological Education, Science, Early Years.

Assessment: continuous

Fees: EU students: £1020 pa
      Non-EU students: £6540 pa

Enquiries: Katherine Barrett; k.barrett@chester.ac.uk; F: 01244 390585

■ **MA/MSc, Diploma, Certificate in Higher Education**

Length of course: *as MEd above*

Entry requirements: *as MEd above*

Course content: A diverse but cohesive range of modules from which participants choose to study. These modules are reviewed annually to reflect the changes in higher education development.

Assessment: continuous

Enquiries: Linda Rush; l.rush@chester.ac.uk; F: 01244 390 585

Fees: EU students: £1500 pa
      Non-EU students: £6540 pa

RESEARCH DEGREES

■ MPhil, PhD

The School offers research supervision in a number of areas, notably SEN, Language & Literacy, Creative & Performing Arts (Art & Drama), ICT, Education Management.

<u>Length of course:</u> *MPhil:* not less than 1 calendar year f/t
  PhD: not less than 2 calendar years f/t

<u>Entry requirements:</u> Normally a good Honours degree (2.1 or above); applications will also be considered on the basis of significant appropriate experience.

<u>Fees:</u> EU students: £2740 f/t (p/t pro rata)
  Non-EU students: £6540 pa

<u>Enquiries:</u> Steve Bartlett; s.bartlett@chester.ac.uk; F: 01244 390 585

*A number of international student **bursaries** (for all levels of study) are available each year. Each award is for £1,000 annually, renewable for a maximum of three years, subject to satisfactory progress.*

UNIVERSITY COLLEGE CHICHESTER

International Programmes
Bognor Regis Campus
Upper Bognor Road
BOGNOR REGIS   PO21 1HR

T: 01243 812081
F: 01243 812081
E: g.lloyd@ucc.ac.uk
W: www.ucc.ac.uk/international

Head of Centre: Stephen Corcoran

BACHELOR DEGREES

■ BA Hons Arts & Humanities with English Language Teaching

Throughout this programme international students are offered an additional alloca-
tion of individual tutorial support and a specialised induction programme to help
them make the transition to study in a new language and new academic culture.
Length of course:
Entry requirements: 1 ELTS 6 or equivalent.
Course content: A course in Arts and Humanities either majoring in or linked to other
subjects as a joint or minor route. Subjects available:
• Business & Management
• Fine Art
• Geography
• History
• Information Technology
• Media Studies
• Music
• Related Arts
• Theology

CERTIFICATES

■ Trinity College London Certificate in TESOL

Length of course: 1 year p/t
Entry requirements: University entrance requirements.
Course content:
• An introduction to the formal aspects of Language
• An examination of the way English is taught
• Classroom skills
• Techniques for putting ideas into practice

OTHER COURSES

■ Teaching Practicum for American Students

Length of course: 1 term (12 weeks)
Entry requirements: Participants will be trainee teachers from the US.
Course content: The Practicum takes place in primary schools in the counties of West
Sussex and Hampshire. Time spent in schools is supported by weekly seminars and a
two-week induction course at the beginning of the programme designed to introduce

students to the local environment and to provide an orientation towards the UK schooling system and its current pressures and expectations.

Fees: £3600 (includes accommodation and most meals)

■ **Short Courses for Language Teachers**
• **Language Development for English Teachers**
• **Teaching English in Secondary Schools**
• **Teaching English to Young Learners**

Length of course: 3 weeks
Entry requirements: Participants should be teaching at secondary or primary level.
Course content: Advanced language improvement and ELT Methodology for Teachers.

■ **Certificate/Diploma in Foundation Studies for International Students**
Length of course: *Certificate:* 1 semester (15 weeks); *Diploma:* 2 semesters (30 weeks)
Entry requirements: High School graduates with IELTS 4-4.5.
Course content: The programme is designed to improve students' English and equip them with necessary skills for entry to degree level study.

■ **Diploma in Practical English Teaching**
This is a fully validated and accredited programme which is conducted in Japan for experienced Japanese teachers of English.
Length of course: 2 years or 1 year fast-track.
Course content: ELT Methodology; English Language Development.
For further details see: www.diploma.or.jp/chichester

■ **Commissioned Teacher Education Programmes**
These are tailor-made and externally commissioned short courses for experienced ELT professionals, including senior administrators and teacher trainers and for teachers from initial to post-experience levels. Courses are conducted in the UK and overseas.
For further details, see our website.

■ **International Educational Partnerships with Overseas Universities**
This programme offers overseas students the opportunity to study for their degree in their own country and one or two years at UCC in the UK. Students either gain a degree at UCC or alternatively credits from UCC can be transferred to their home university.
Course content: Students study a main subject such as Business Studies, Law Studies, English Studies or TEFL. In addition, they follow an integrated programme of advanced language development, content study and study skills.
For further details, see our website.

■ **Year/Semester Abroad Programmes**
Overseas students who wish to spend a year or semester abroad, can arrange for their home university to credit the modules they study at UCC.
For further details, see our website.

DE MONTFORT UNIVERSITY

School of Education
Polhill Campus
Polhill Avenue
BEDFORD MK41 9EA

T: 01234 793334
F: 01234 793277
E: ppankhurst@dmu.ac.uk
W: www.dmu.ac.uk

Enquiries: Pat Pankhurst, Admissions *(contact details see above)*

De Montfort University is one of the largest providers of Teacher Education in the United Kingdom. The School of Education is part of an exciting new Faculty of Education and Sports Science, which has its main site in the historic town of Bedford. The Faculty enjoys the facilities of a multi-million pound learning resource centre providing a variety of learning media including state of the art Information and Communications Technology.

The School of Education has an enviable reputation for providing high quality degree programmes that incorporate new knowledge and national developments in education. The *Bachelor of Education* degree programmes are run in close collaboration with a network of schools. Graduates enjoy excellent employment prospects. The *MA Learning and Teaching* is a highly successful programme for those teaching in Further and Higher Education. The *MA Education* offers a wide variety of modules which address contemporary educational issues. The *MA Education: Educational Management* will be of interest to those engaged in school leadership, management and administration, at a variety of levels. The *MA Education: Dyslexia Studies* explores exciting developments in research into dyslexia. The *MA Education: Art and Design Education* is taught by staff who are accomplished artists and who regularly exhibit their own work. All courses draw on the developing research interests of staff, creating a thriving research culture from which postgraduate students benefit.

Degree programmes recognise credit accumulation and transfer schemes. Applicants may seek accreditation for prior learning, subject to the University's regulations. The School of Education has close links with other institutions in the UK, Europe and beyond.

BACHELOR DEGREES

■ BEd Hons Primary with QTS

Length of course: 4 years f/t

Entry requirements: 2 A-levels and 5 GCSEs at grade C or above including Maths, English Language and Science or equivalents.

Course content: The course consists of four key elements:

• *Core Subject Specialism*

Students study and become specialists in one subject from English, Maths and Science and one from Art, Geography History PE, Technology and Advanced Early Years.

• *Curriculum Studies (Core and Foundations Subjects)*

Students are prepared to teach the core curriculum subjects of English, Maths and Sciences and are introduced to the foundation subjects of History, Geography, PE, Music, Art & Design, Design Technology, ICT, RE.

Glossary on page XI

• *Professional and Educational Studies*
Students develop skills and knowledge needed for primary teaching. Issues considered include: Child development, how children learn, planning for learning, primary schools, classroom management and control, special educational needs, assessment, class, gender, ethnicity.
• *School-based Experience*
Students spend some 160 days in school over the four years of study.

■ **BA Educational Studies (Joint or Combined)**
This course is a fascinating experience in its own right, but will be specially useful for those intending to progress to a PGCE.
Length of course: 3 years f/t
Entry requirements: 2 A-levels and 5 GCSEs at grade C or above or equivalent.
Course content: The course can be taken in combination with one or two other subjects. It looks at how people develop and learn, the history and organisation of the education system of England and Wales and the values and ideas which inform educational debate. There are modules available in the history, politics, sociology, psychology and philosophy of education and others which focus on issues such as gender, race and ethnicity.

■ **BA Hons Physical Education with QTS (Secondary)**
Length of course: 4 years f/t
Entry requirements: 2 A-levels and 5 GCSEs at grade C or above, including Maths and English Language or equivalents; one-day interviews including a practical assessment and a short written test.
Course content: In the first two years there is a varied programme of Physical Education covering all the major sports, including gymnastics, dance, athletics, swimming and outdoor pursuits. The theory elements include: Physiology, Anatomy and Kinesiology, Biomechanics, Psychology, History and Sociology of PE and Sport. The Professional Studies component runs through all four years and there are substantial blocks of school experience where students practise and develop their teaching skills.

CERTIFICATES / DIPLOMAS

■ **PGCE Primary**
This programme is run in partnership with local schools and prepares graduates to teach the 5-7 or 7-11 age ranges.
Length of course: 1 year f/t (38 weeks)
Entry requirements: At least a second class honours degree, which should contain the equivalent of 18 months of study in a subject relevant to the Primary National Curriculum (this is the subject in which trainees intend to become a curriculum leader); GCSE grade C or above in English, Maths and, if you were born after 1 Sept. 1979, Science; some experience working with children.
Course content: The programme is divided between study at the University and placements in schools. The major subjects studied are: English, Maths, Science, Professional Studies, ICT. Trainees are also introduced to: Art & Design, D&T, Geography, History, Music, PE, RE.

During the three school placements trainees have an increasing responsibility for a whole class.

Assessment: A trainee's knowledge and competence as a classroom teacher is judged by:

- performance in the final school placement
- six written assignments (two in each of English, Maths, Science)
- satisfactory completion of a profile demonstrating that the standards for newly qualified teachers have been met

Applications: *through the GTTR (see glossary)*

▪ PGCE Secondary

Length of course: 1 year f/t (36 weeks)

Entry requirements: A first degree awarded by an approved University in a subject specialism (or allied area) appropriate to the National Curriculum; GCSE grade C or above or equivalent in English and Maths.

Course content: Subject areas offered:

- Art & Design
- Dance
- D&T
- English
- Maths
- PE
- Science

For 24 weeks of the course trainees are based in schools. They are introduced to fundamental classroom skills at an early stage and are expected to take full responsibility for planning and delivering teaching sessions as they make progress through the course. School experience is supervised by school-based staff (subject mentors) who have the relevant training, support and subject expertise.

The time in University affords student teachers opportunities to reflect on their work in schools and to share ideas and experiences with student colleagues. Throughout the course, student teachers compile a Profile of Professional Standards which documents progress and indicates personal qualities.

The training salary applies to this course.

Assessment: There are no formal written examinations and assessment is based on achieving the Standards set out in Government Circular *Qualifying to Teach.*

Applications: *through the GTTR (see glossary)*

▪ Certificate in Education/PGCE Post-compulsory Education

This is a single course which can be taken at two academic levels. It leads on from the City and Guilds 7307 course and can lead into the MA Learning and Teaching. Students specify at enrolment which award they are aiming for, but can change from one to the other at a later point (this may, however, involve additional work and costs).

Length of course: 2 years

Entry requirements: *Certificate:* Candidates must be engaged in teaching in post-compulsory (ie post-16) education for at least 60 hours per year, have suitable qualifications in the subject they teach (at least BTEC National Diploma or NVQ Level 3) and/or can produce evidence of other study at a comparable level. *PGCE:* In addition to the above, candidates must hold a degree from a UK university (normally 2.2 or above) or its equivalent.

Course content: There are two stages to the programme:

Stage 1 provides a practical and general introduction to
- Preparing to Teach
- The Teaching and Learning Process
- Assessing Teaching and Learning

Stage 2 builds on the understandings and skills of Stage 1 and provides more opportunities to relate the taught material to the student's chosen area of practice.

Throughout the programme, students take *Professional Discipline* and *Observed Practice*, modules which are mainly individually tutored and serve to apply and integrate the learning from other modules.

Assessment: In each module students demonstrate through a portfolio of work or a project that they meet the specified Learning Outcomes.

MASTER'S DEGREES

■ MA Learning & Teaching

This part-time programme is aimed at professionals working in institutions and organisations in which learning and teaching is a central part of their task. Intermediate awards at postgraduate Certificate and Diploma levels are offered.

Entry requirements: A degree or degree-equivalent qualification awarded by a recognised institution; evidence of relevant teaching work. Holders of a non-graduate Certificate in Education in Further or Higher Education may be admitted, subject to demonstration that they can benefit from the programme and are likely to complete it successfully.

Course content: The course is designed to:
- be directly relevant to the participant's work
- enable participants to gain credit for their existing knowledge and skills and to develop further skills
- increase participants' understanding of learning and teaching processes and their management
- develop participants' competence and confidence in all aspects of the teaching and tutoring role
- expand participants' repertoire of working approaches
- enable participants to apply theory to current practice and to develop and extend practice through action research

Assessment: On the basis of claiming credit for the achievement of specified learning outcomes for each module.

■ MA Education

This is a modular course intended for professionals actively involved in teaching, educational leadership and organisation in all phases and at all levels. It will be of particular interest to classroom teachers, headteachers, deputy headteachers, curriculum managers, phase and key stage leaders, heads of departments, subject leaders and professionals working in local education authority advisory services.

Intermediate awards at Certificate and Diploma levels are also offered.

Length of course: 1 year f/t; 3-6 years p/t
Entry requirements: A degree or degree equivalent awarded by a recognised university and QTS (eg PGCE, Certificate in Education) or substantial experience in an appropriate educational field. Non-graduates with QTS may be admitted if they have either a Diploma in Education and/or substantial teaching experience.
Course structure: The course is flexible and can relate to the student's own chosen focus, teaching or area of professional responsibility. Much of the student's study will be school-focused.
Assessment: Each module is assessed through professionally-based tasks and negotiated projects. For the award of MA a 20,000-word dissertation is required.

- **MA Education: Educational Management**

This is a modular programme for teachers and others engaged in educational leadership. Credit accumulation is based on University-based and distance learning modules, negotiated workplace study and participation in selected LEA CPD portfolio courses. Intermediate awards at postgraduate Certificate and Diploma levels are offered.
Entry requirements: A degree or degree equivalent awarded by a recognised university and QTS (eg PGCE, Certificate in Education). Non-graduates with QTS may be admitted if they have a Diploma in Education and/or substantial teaching experience, including an aspect of educational management.
Assessment: Each module is assessed through professionally-based tasks and negotiated projects. For the award of MA a 20,000-word dissertation is required.

- **MA Education: Dyslexia Studies**

Exciting developments in research into dyslexia in Britain and abroad make this degree most opportune, particularly as few programmes deal with dyslexia at this level. The programme is of interest to graduates, experienced teachers and trainers from compulsory, further and higher education seeking to synthesise their theoretical understanding of dyslexia and its concomitants with their professional practice. In addition, it provides a sound basis for postgraduate study and career specialisation. It produces graduates with practical, analytical and interpersonal qualities and skills that meet the demands of high-quality support for dyslexic learners.
Entry requirements: A degree award by CNAA or a UK university or a recognised equivalent qualification and QTS (eg PGCE, a teaching certificate or other equivalent teaching qualification). Recent experience in lecturing, teaching or training involving support in an appropiate field, is essential. Two academic referees are required to support an application. An interview may also be required. For non-graduates, acceptance normally requires QTS (eg Certificate of Education) plus supporting staff development with recent and substantial experience in an appropriate field. Other qualifications from recognised bodies are also considered.
Course structure: The programme provides a practice-led study, organised around a modular structure, permitting some flexibility in study patterns. It offers three levels of award by credit accumulation.
Assessment: By module assignments.

■ MA Education: Art & Design Education

This is a full-time and part-time modular programme with intermediate awards of Postgraduate Certificate or Postgraduate Diploma. It is intended for experienced teachers of Art and Design and for lecturers, advisors and curriculum developers and for postgraduates who have an appropriate degree in the visual arts but no teaching experience.

Length of course: 1.5 years f/t; 3 years p/t

Entry requirements: A relevant (ie visual arts and design subjects) honours degree of CNAA or a UK university or its recognised equivalent, QTS or approved teaching experience. Applicants are normally invited to interview. Overseas candidates may be required to submit written work and photographs in place of an interview.

Course content/structure: A choice of modules from:
• Approaches to the Study of Art & Design
• Theories and Practices in Art & Design
• ICT in Art & Design Education
• Research Design and Methodologies

Most taught modules are offered on weekday evenings, but it is also possible to negotiate independent and school-based study in some modules to the student's professional situation.

Assessment: Typically by submission of a 5000-word assignment or a seminar or other presentation supported by a shorter report. For the award of MA a 20,000-word dissertation is required.

UNIVERSITY OF DURHAM

School of Education
Leazes Road
DURHAM   DH1 1TA

T: 0191 374 2000
F: 0191 374 3506
W: www.dur.ac.uk/~ded0www/

Head of School: Professor Richard Gott
Enquiries: Lynn Carrington; lynn.carrington@durham.ac.uk; T: 0191 374 1732; F: 0191 374 3506

BACHELOR DEGREES

■ BA Hons Primary Education
Length of course: 3 years f/t
Entry requirements: At least grades CCC at A-level or equivalent (2 AS levels are acceptable in place of 1 A-level); GCSE (grades A-C) in Maths, English Language and Science or equivalents.
Course content: There are two major components to the course: academic and professional. The academic component involves developing an in-depth knowledge and understanding of the core subjects of the National Curriculum and the opportunity to become a curriculum specialist in English, Maths, Science or ICT. The professional component focuses on the professional standards required for the award of Qualified Teacher Status. This includes 33 weeks of school experience in a variety of schools and a programme addressing whole-school issues which affect the learning environment of the child.

■ BA Hons Education Studies
Length of course: 3 years f/t
Entry requirements: A minimum of grade B at A-level or equivalent in chosen subject (see course content). Applications welcomed from mature students and those with non-standard qualifications. It is expected that students will have a strong interest in continuing one of their A-level subjects and a desire to explore issues such as philosophy, psychology, sociology and politics.
Course content/structure: Students combine the study of education (50%) with the study in another university department (50%). Possible combinations are: Education Studies with one of the following:
• Biological Sciences
• English Studies
• Geography
• History
• Linguistics
• Music
(Other subjects may be offered - contact Admissions Tutor for details.)
Students take three modules per year in each of the two departments.

CERTIFICATES / DIPLOMAS

■ Postgraduate Diploma in Counselling Studies
Length of course: 1 year f/t; 2 years p/t (Kenya only)
Entry requirements: Usually a degree but other qualifications may be acceptable.

Applicants will be asked to provide evidence of their ability to study at postgraduate level.

Course content: Course experience and group membership on this course are the same as for students on the MA Counselling Studies course (see below), but the assessment criteria for the components of the course are less demanding at Diploma level. Students may be permitted to change to the MA on the basis of initial course work.

■ PGCE Primary/Elementary

Length of course: 1 year

Entry requirements: Degree in a subject relevant to the elementary school curriculum from a recognised university; suitable previous experience with children, a wide range of interests and appropriate personal qualities.

Course content: The course prepares students to teach in primary/elementary schools, specialising in either The Early Years (ages 4-8) or The Junior Years (ages 7-12). It offers:

- Teaching experience and practice in local schools in the North East of England
- Experience of a close partnership between students, university tutors and teachers in schools
- Knowledge of a variety of stimulating approaches to learning
- Study using workshops, small tutorial groups, lecturers and practical work
- The opportunity to exchange ideas and experiences with students, teachers and tutors from other backgrounds.

The course includes:

- Methods of Teaching
- Cross-curricular Issues
- Professional Studies
- Teaching & Learning Processes
- Classroom Management
- Special Educational Needs
- Health Education & the Environment
- Assessment Techniques in the Classroom
- Evaluation
- Teaching practice

Assessment: Written assignments set by the student's tutors, a teaching practice file and supervised work in the classroom.

■ PGCE Secondary

Length of course: 1 year

Entry requirements: Degree in chosen subject from a recognised university; suitable previous experience with children, a wide range of interests and appropriate personal qualities.

Course content: The course prepares students to teach in secondary/high schools (ages 11-18). It offers:

- Teaching experience and practice in local schools in the North East of England
- Experience of a close partnership between students, university tutors and teachers in schools

- Knowledge of a variety of stimulating approaches to learning
- Study using workshops, small tutorial groups, lecturers and practical work
- The opportunity to exchange ideas and experiences with students, teachers and tutors from other backgrounds.

Students specialise in one of the following: Biology, Chemistry, Drama, English, Geography, History, Maths, Modern Languages, Music, PE, Physics, RE

The course includes:

- Specialist teaching methods taught in the University School of Education and in local schools
- Whole school issues and professional studies
- Classroom Management
- Special Educational Needs
- Equal Opportunities
- Multi-cultural Education
- Assessment Techniques in the Classroom
- Evaluation and Teaching Practice

Assessment: Written assignments set by the student's tutors, a teaching practice file and supervised work in the classroom.

MASTER'S DEGREES

■ MA(Ed) Modular Programme
Length of course: 1 year f/t; up to 5 years by modular study
Entry requirements: Usually a degree, but other qualifications may be acceptable.
Course content: A course for graduates who wish to study a taught course at postgraduate level. It is designed to provide teachers and others with a professional interest in education with an opportunity to broaden and deepen their existing knowledge and to equip them to take up positions of responsibility. The degree is particularly designed for those seeking leadership positions at various levels in education. Modules are taught out of term time for ease of attendance.

■ MA(Ed) with QTS Primary or Secondary
Length of course: 1 year f/t plus up to 5 years p/t
Entry requirements: Usually a degree, but other qualifications may be acceptable.
Course content: A new, innovative route to an MA in Education that incorporates the 1-year full-time PGCE Primary or Secondary course, takes account of the induction year for newly qualified teachers and concludes with the presentation of a dissertation and award of MA(Ed) at the end of the second year of teaching. The part-time second and third year modules are taught over weekends for ease of attendance.

■ MA Counselling Studies
Length of course: 1 year f/t; 2 years p/t (Kenya only)
Entry requirements: Usually a degree, but other qualifications may be acceptable.
Course content: This course is for those who wish to improve their knowledge of counselling and their ability to function effectively in a counselling relationship. The course is experiential, that is, it offers opportunities to do and feel as well as to think. The overall aim of the course is to enable the individual to improve his or her practice and understanding of guidance and counselling. This is achieved by means of four

parallel components, each of which is assessed:
- Counselling psychology
- A research project
- Study of the practice of counselling
- Study of the psychology of the self and relationships

RESEARCH DEGREES

■ MA, MEd, PhD

Length of course: MA: 1 year f/t; 2 years p/t

MEd: 2 years f/t; 1 year f/t plus 1 year p/t; 3 years p/t

PhD: 3 years f/t; 6 years p/t

Candidates for research degrees are accepted in a wide range of areas of special interest to members of staff. The School has a supportive approach to supervision of research and research seminars are held regularly on a wide variety of subjects.

■ EdD

Length of course: 3 years f/t; up to 6 years p/t

Entry requirements: Usually a Masters degree although specially approved qualifications may be acceptable.

Course content: This taught doctorate in Education offers a rigorous, structured programme of six taught units and a supervised thesis in response to the radical changes in Education. It allows senior Education professionals to obtain a critical understanding of a number of key issues rather than of one only. The taught units provide an in-depth study of the theories and practices of six main Education themes at doctoral level, while the thesis gives the traditional research skills, critical acumen, theoretical grasp and insights into practice usually associated with a PhD. The course modules are taught either at weekend schools or at two summer schools.

The degree is also offered in Hong Kong and Singapore. The content of the course is essentially the same but focuses on local issues relevant to the students' work. The thesis is supervised by correspondence and annual visits by supervisors.

FEES

EU students: *Postgraduate Certificate in Education:* £1470

Other Postgraduate courses: £2945 pa f/t; £1470 pa p/t

First degree courses: £1075 pa

Non-EU students: *(all courses)* £7640 pa f/t; £2468 pa p/t

Exceptions:
- Postgraduate Diploma in Counselling (Kenya): £2000 pa p/t (2-year course)
- MA (Ed) modular programme: £262 per module; £524 dissertation
- MA (Ed) with QTS programme: *as per MA (Ed) modular programme*
- EdD Hong Kong & Singapore: £13,860 (paid over 4 years)
- EdD Summer School Programme: £10,800 (paid over 4 years)

UNIVERSITY OF EAST ANGLIA

School of Education and Professional Development   T: 01603 592855
University Plain   F: 01603 593446
NORWICH   NR4 7TJ   E: eduinfo@uea.ac.uk
     W: www.uea.ac.uk/edu/

Dean of School: Dr Anne Cockburn

The School of Education and Professional Development, incorporating the Centre for Applied Research in Education (CARE), has an excellent research record. It is housed in purpose-built accommodation on the University campus which occupies an attractive parkland site on the edge of the historic City of Norwich. The School has established an international reputation for enquiry-based learning, educational evaluation and curriculum development.

The School offers a range of postgraduate programmes, advanced courses and research degrees for students from overseas. In addition to its established programmes, the School of Education welcomes discussions with educational organisations from overseas with a view to assisting in their professional development programmes.

CERTIFICATES / DIPLOMAS

■ PGCE

This course is intended to prepare candidates for teaching in the UK.
Length of course: 1 year f/t
Fees: EU students: £1075
     Non-EU students: £9350
Enquiries: The School Clerk (address see above); eduinfo@uea.ac.uk

■ Diploma in Counselling

This course is designed to equip successful students to practice professionally as counsellors. It is approved by the British Association for Counselling.
Length of course: 1 year f/t
Course content: Students undertake substantial practical work, including clinical placements under the supervision of the University Counselling Service.
Fees: EU students: £5170
     Non-EU students: £7250
Enquiries: The School Clerk (address see above); eduinfo@uea.ac.uk

MASTER'S DEGREES

■ MA Advanced Educational Practice
■ MA in Education
■ MA Counselling Studies

Length of courses: MA AEP: 3 years p/t; other MAs: 1 year f/t
Assessment: Assignments and dissertation.
Fees: EU students: £2805 f/t; £1405 p/t
     Non-EU students: £7250 f/t; £3825 p/t
Enquiries: The International Office (address see above); e.chapman@uea.ac.uk

RESEARCH DEGREES

The School can accommodate a wide range of research interests for both full- and part-time students. Specialisms within the School include:
• Action Research
• Evaluation
• Curriculum Development
Additionally the School offers a biennial taught doctorate (EdD) and delivers a part-time PhD programme in Hong Kong.

Length of courses:
Research programmes: 1, 2 or 3 years f/t; 2, 4 or 6 years p/t
EdD: 4 years
HK PhD: 6 years
Fees: EU students: £2805 f/t; £1405 p/t
     Non-EU students: £7250 f/t; £3825 p/t
     HK PhD: £4870pa p/t

OTHER COURSES

■ **Short Courses / Consultancies**

The School offers a wide range of short courses and consultancies that can be negotiated. Central areas of expertise are:
• Educational Change
• Distance Learning
• In-service Training
• Education for Development
• Programme Evaluation
• University Development
• TEFL/TESL/ELT
The School also accepts academics from a range of countries as Professional Associates.

UNIVERSITY OF EAST LONDON

School of Education &
  Community Studies
Longbridge Road
BARKING   RM8 2AS

T: 020 8223 2150
F: 020 8223 2882

Centre for Institutional Studies
Maryland House
Manbey Park Road
LONDON   E15 1EY

E: j.l.pash@uel.ac.uk
W: www.uel.ac.uk

The University of East London (UEL) has three campuses within easy reach of both Central London and Essex countryside. The university has been involved in Education and Community Studies and in Initial Teacher Training for many years and our programmes have been recognised nationwide and world wide as being innovative, supportive and responsive to educational needs.

The University welcomes overseas students into an exciting academic environment. East London is made up of communities with cultures from all over the world, with a great variety of beliefs, languages, customs, food and dress. The University reflects this diversity among its students.

BACHELOR DEGREES

Undergraduate Modular Programmes:
- **BA Education & Community Programmes**
- **BSc Information & Communication Technology in Education**
- **BA Language in Education**
- **BA Early Childhood Studies**
- **BA Linguistics**
- **BA English Language Studies**
- **BA TESOL** *(currently under validation)*

Length of courses: 3 years f/t or p/t

Enquiries: John Trushell; j.m.trushell@uel.ac.uk; T: 020 8223 2154
           Debbie Brearley; d.brearley@uel.ac.uk; T: 020 8223 2729

CERTIFICATES / DIPLOMAS

- **PGCE Primary** (Foundation Stage/Key Stage 1 or Key Stage 1 and Key Stage 2)
- **PGCE Secondary** (ages 11-16 - Design & Technology, English, Mathematics, Science, Modern Foreign Languages)

Both PGCE courses prepare student teachers to work effectively in inner-city multicultural schools. There is a particular focus on inclusive education and working with bilingual children. Applicants from communities under-represented in the teaching profession are particularly welcome.

Length of course: *Primary:* 38 weeks f/t; *Secondary:* 36 weeks f/t

Enquiries: Frances Brodie; f.l.brodie@uel.ac.uk; T: 020 8223 2832 (Primary)
           Kate Tuerena; k.tuerena:uel.ac.uk; T: 020 8223 2782 (Secondary)

Website: www.uel.ac.uk/pgce

- **PGCE/CertEd in Post-Compulsory Education & Training** *(currently under validation)*

Length of course: 1 year f/t

Enquiries: Hazel Cross; cross@uel.ac.uk; T: 020 8223 2395

Glossary on page XI

MASTER'S DEGREES

The postgraduate modular structure gives flexibility to meet the needs of individual students. The pathways are listed below:

- **MA Primary Education Practice**
  Modules in:
  - Improving Primary Education (compulsory)
  - Primary Literacy in Practice
  - Maths in Primary Education
  - Special Educational Needs in Practice
  - The Early Years in Practice
  - Professional Development
  - Bilingualism in Education
  - Primary ICT

Enquiries: Fozya Sharif; f.sharif@uel.ac.uk; T: 020 8223 2738
- **MA Professional Practice in Education**
- **MA Voluntary Sector Studies**
- **MSc Public and Community Service**

Enquiries: Cornel DaCosta; c.dacosta@uel.ac.uk; T: 020 8223 2269

- **MA Linguistics by Independent Study**

Enquiries: John Simpson; t.j.simpson@uel.ac.uk; T: 020 8223 2245

RESEARCH DEGREES

- **MPhil/PhD**

The Department has extensive experience of supervising students preparing for the degrees of MPhil and PhD. Current and past areas of research include:
- Education for Children with Special Needs
- Education Management
- Voluntary Organisations & Volunteering
- Theory of Adult Basic Education Policy-Making
- Higher Education
- Teacher Education & Early Childhood

Enquiries: Helen Penn; h.penn@uel.ac.uk

OTHER COURSES

- **University Certificate in English Language Studies for Higher Education**
  (currently under validation)

Enquiries: John Simpson; t.j.simpson@uel.ac.uk; T: 020 8223 2245

- **Individual modules** from the modular postgraduate programme are available as short courses. They cover a range of primary curriculum issues.
Fees: Vary depending on the number of students involved and when and how the courses are taught.
Enquiries: Helen Mitchell; h.mitchell@uel.ac.uk; T: 020 8223 2157

- **Short courses to specific requirements**
Enquiries: Mike Locke; m.locke@uel.ac.uk; T: 020 8223 4203

UNIVERSITY OF EDINBURGH

Faculty of Education
Holyrood Road
EDINBURGH   EH8 8AQ

T: 0131 651 6138
F: 0131 651 6052
E: education.faculty@ed.ac.uk
W: www.education.ed.ac.uk

Dean of Faculty: Professor Gordon Kirk

BACHELOR DEGREES

■ BEd Hons Design & Technology
Length of course: 4 years f/t
Entry requirements: Equivalent of 2 A-level passes at grade C. GCSE or equivalent passes at grade C in Maths, English Language and English Literature and in two subjects other than those at A-level. Selection normally involves an interview.
Course content: The programme enables students to teach at Secondary school level and develops key areas of the teacher's skill range such as technological capability and knowledge and understanding of the nature, principles, and processes of education which affect and inform learning and teaching practices. Professional placement in schools forms a substantial part of the programme.
Assessment: Based on a combination of examination, course work, dissertation and teaching practice.
Fees: *EU students:* £1075 pa f/t; *Non-EU students:* £7460 pa f/t
Enquiries: peter.barrett@ed.ac.uk

■ BEd Hons Physical Education
Length of course: 4 years f/t
Entry requirements: Equivalent of 2 A-level passes at grade C. GCSE or equivalent passes at grade C in Maths, English Language and English Literature and in two subjects other than those at A-level. Selection normally involves an interview.
Course content: In each year of the programme students develop their knowledge and understanding of the PE curriculum through involvement in a range of physical activities and the study of human development and physical activity from three theoretical perspectives. Professional placement in secondary schools forms a substantial part of the programme
Assessment: Based on a combination of examination, course work, dissertation and teaching practice.
Fees: *EU students:* £1075 pa f/t; *Non-EU students:* £7460 pa f/t
Enquiries: peter.hill@ed.ac.uk

■ BEd Hons Primary Education
Length of course: 4 years f/t
Entry requirements: Equivalent of 2 A-level passes at grade C. GCSE or equivalent passes at grade B in Maths and grade C in English Language and English Literature and in two subjects other than those at A-level. Selection normally involves an interview.
Course content: The programme is designed to provide professional preparation for teaching children of the 3-12 years age range covering the core of the Scottish Primary curriculum. Professional placement in schools forms a substantial part of the programme.
Assessment: Based on a combination of examination, course work, dissertation and teaching practice.

Glossary on page XI

Fees: *EU students:* £1075 pa f/t; *Non-EU students:* £7460 pa f/t
Enquiries: nigel.parton@ed.ac.uk

CERTIFICATES / DIPLOMAS

■ PGCE Primary & Secondary Education
Length of course: 36 weeks
Entry requirements: Applicants must have a degree validated by a UK university or a degree of an equivalent standard from an institution outside the UK. For Secondary teaching the degree should normally contain passes in a minimum of three teaching subject qualifying courses (TSQC) in the subject or subjects the student wants to teach. One TSQC must be at Scottish degree level two or above and one at level three or above, or equivalent. Applicants must also have GCSE or equivalent passes at grade C in English Language and English Literature and, for Primary teaching, grade B in Maths. Selection involves an interview.
Course content: The programmes seek, in one academic year, to train students to become Primary teachers or subject teachers in Secondary schools as appropriate. The programmes are 36 weeks in length, divided into a first term of 16 weeks and two further 10-week terms, with the normal starting date at the end of August/beginning of September. Study is divided between university-based learning and practical experience in schools in the Edinburgh and general Lothian area. As well as Primary Teaching, the following Secondary subjects are available: Art & Design, Biology, Chemistry, Computing, Drama, English, Geography, History, Maths, MFL (French, German, Spanish, Italian), Modern Studies, Music, PE, Physics, RE, Technological Education.
Fees: *EU students:* £1075 pa f/t; *Non-EU students:* £6990 pa f/t
Enquiries: don.skinner@ed.ac.uk (Primary); tony.gemmell@ed.ac.uk (Secondary)

MASTER'S DEGREES

■ MSc Education
Length of course: 12 months f/t; 24-36 months p/t
Entry requirements: Applicants should be graduates or have graduate equivalent qualifications with relevant professional experience.
Course content: The course provides a range of about 20 options from which six are chosen according to interest and purpose.
Assessment: By course work and dissertation.
Fees: *EU students:* £2805 pa f/t; *Non-EU students:* £7460 pa f/t
Enquiries: g.donn@ed.ac.uk

■ MSc by Research (Education)
Length of course: 12 months f/t; 24-36 months p/t
Entry requirements: Second-class honours degree or equivalent in a relevant discipline.
Course content: Students follow a course of specialist research training before completing a dissertation. As well as being a free-standing degree it is also recognised as a first year of doctoral study.
Assessment: By course work and dissertation.

Fees: *EU students:* £2805 pa f/t; *Non-EU students:* £7460 pa f/t
Enquiries: pat.mclaughlin@ed.ac.uk

■ **Modular Master's Scheme (MMS)**
Length of course: 12 months f/t; 72 months p/t
Entry requirements: Applicants should be graduates or have graduate equivalent qualifications with relevant professional experience.
Course content: The scheme offers flexible opportunities to combine modules for the awards of Postgraduate Certificate (4 modules), Diploma (8 modules) or Master's Degree (8 modules plus dissertation) in a variety of areas, although not all Master's awards are available to full-time students. Programmes open to overseas applicants include:

• TESOL (by class contact and distance learning)
• Education Support
• Counselling
• Management of Training & Development
• Advanced Professional Studies
• Advanced Studies in Education
• Music Therapy (Nordoff-Robbins)
• Difficulties with Literacy Development
• Outdoor Education, Sport Management, Performance Psychology, Performance Coaching, Strength & Conditioning, Young People's PE, Sport & Exercise

Fees: EU students: £185 per module
      Non-EU students: £620 per module *(to be confirmed)*

RESEARCH DEGREES

■ **MPhil, PhD**
Length of course: *MPhil:* 24 months f/t; 48 months p/t
                  PhD: 36 months f/t; 72 months p/t
Entry requirements: Good first degree; research potential shown by a sound proposal.
Research areas:
• Classroom Learning
• Community Education
• Curriculum Theory
• Disaffection from School
• Educational Administration
• International Education
• Learning Difficulties
• Learning & Teaching in Higher Education
• Philosophy & Policy
• Physical Education, Sport & Leisure Studies
• Sociology of Education
• Teachers & Teaching
• Teaching English to Speakers of Other Languages
Fees: *EU students:* £2805 pa f/t; *Non-EU students:* £7460 pa f/t
Enquiries: b.barber@ed.ac.uk

School of Education & Lifelong Learning   T: 01392 264815
Heavitree Road   F: 01392 264902
EXETER EX1 2LU   E: ed-cpd@exeter.ac.uk
W: www.exeter.ac.uk/education

<u>Enquiries:</u> Graduate Studies Office *(contact details above)*

The University of Exeter's School of Education and Lifelong Learning is one of the most diverse and highly regarded in the country. Our Graduate Studies Programme is committed to providing excellence in continuing professional development (CPD) and research. Whether an intensive short course, masters degree or research degree, our academic staff are leaders in their fields and their expertise has been recognised by government examiners. The latest QAA inspection awarded our CPD provision a perfect score of 24, a testament to the quality of our teaching and support. Our research is also highly regarded as evidenced by a 5 in the 2001 RAE. Considered one of the most beautiful campuses in Britain, the University of Exeter is situated in the heart of Devon. With its lush rolling green hills, beaches and national parks, it is no wonder that Exeter is consistently regarded as one of the best places to live in the UK. The School offers a special welcome to international students with encouragement to participate in every aspect of student life.

DIPLOMAS / MASTER'S DEGREES

Each of the following full-time courses are available for study at both the Postgraduate Diploma (PgDip) and Masters' Degree (MEd) level.

■ PgDip/MEd TEFL
This course is designed for teachers of English as a second or foreign language.
<u>Course content:</u>
- Theory of language
- Language learning
- Methodology of language teaching
- Language syllabus design
- Language testing
- Sociolinguistics
- Research methods

<u>Enquiries:</u> Sarah Rich; s.a.l.rich@exeter.ac.uk

■ PgDip/MEd Creative Arts Education
Students have wide-ranging opportunities to develop their own work in music, dance, drama or visual arts and also to explore current thinking and practice in creative arts education.
<u>Course content:</u> Each course is based on seminars and studio work, where students are expected to develop their own specialism and also to broaden their artistic horizons and develop new skills. Students undertake an intensive investigation of a theme related to the aims of the course, involving placement and/or visits to schools, colleges or other artistic and educational establishments. The courses are designed to develop the practical artistic skills and theoretical understanding of teachers from the princi-

pal fields of arts education. Emphasis is given to the relationship of the arts to each other and to the school curriculum as a whole. The course also examines the educational use of the arts to meet special needs and the changing role of arts education in a multi-cultural society.

Enquiries: Linda Rolfe; l.m.rolfe@exeter.ac.uk

- **PgDip/MEd Special Educational Needs**

Course content: This course offers advanced study of the special educational needs of learners in both mainstream and special settings. It prepares teachers and those in senior management or advisory/coordinator posts for work in the field of SEN. The course provides students with a critical understanding and reflective experience of cross-phase provision (Early Years, Primary, Secondary and Tertiary). Students will also be able to specialise in one area of interest.

Enquiries: Dr Philip Bayliss; p.d.bayliss@exeter.ac.uk

For all PgDip / MEd courses:

Entry requirements: Applicants typically have a background of successful study to degree level or equivalent, as well as two years professional experience.

Fees: EU students: £2875 (provisional)
         Non-EU students: £7650

- **MSc Educational Research**

Length of course: 1 year f/t; 2 years p/t

Course aims: This ESRC-recognised course prepares students for the independent conduct of educational research. For doctoral students the programme is designed to provide high quality training, both to enable them to carry out their doctoral research and to equip them to pursue, subsequently, other research activities by working systematically through the following stages: theory, methodology, practical investigation and dissemination.

Course structure: Each taught module is 30 hours contact time, usually over a period of 10 weeks.

Assessment: Each 30-credit module has a 4000-word assignment, which is the culmination of formative assignments, plus a 10,000-word dissertation.

Fees: EU students: £2875
         Non-EU students: £7650

RESEARCH DEGREES

The School of Education embraces a considerable variety of research activity, from large-funded programmes to small-scale collaborations with local teachers. A major strength is that because of its size and the fact that it is not wedded to any one type of research paradigm, the School can offer research supervision in nearly all areas of educational research.

The School offers a broad-based research training which complements the subject-specific training given by individual supervisors. This Research Methodology Course involves the completion of assignments which form part of the requirements for conversion from MPhil to PhD. Wherever possible, students become part of a group with similar research interests which provides ongoing support.

Applications covering a wide range of research areas are considered and suitable students are accepted, provided appropriate supervision is available. For more information on specific areas of interest, please contact the School or visit the website.

■ MPhil

Length of course: 2 years f/t; 3 years p/t
Normally students are under the supervision of a member of the academic staff. Regular contact between staff and student must be maintained throughout the period of study.
Entry requirements: Normally a good honours degree in a relevant field; special cases will be considered.
Assessment: 60,000-word thesis.
Fees: EU students: £2875 f/t; £1440 p/t
         Non-EU students: £7650 f/t; 3825 p/t

■ PhD

It is normal practice to be registered on an MPhil degree with a view to transfer to PhD given satisfactory progress.
Length of course: 3-4 years f/t (incl. time registered as MPhil student)
                          4-7 years p/t (incl. time registered as MPhil student)
Entry requirements: Normally a Master's degree with a substantial research component or transfer from MPhil (transfer usually takes place after the equivalent of one year of full-time MPhil research and involves satisfying a small committee)
Assessment: Thesis (not more than 100,000 words without specific prior approval from the Board of the Faculty)
Fees: see MPhil above

■ EdD

A structured modular programme. The degree is specifically directed toward professional development through research and is therefore of particular relevance to experienced practitioners in education. Currently programmes are available in:
• Educational Psychology (weekend courses in Exeter)
• Maths Education
• Professional Studies
• Teaching English as a Foreign Language (conducted by intensive courses of 4 to 5 weeks, held either at Exeter or in the student's home country)
Length of course: 2 years (min) f/t; 4 years (min) p/t
Entry requirements: A Master's degree (the EdD in Educational Psychology requires a degree in Education Psychology) and at least 3 years relevant professional experience.
Assessment: 40,000-word thesis
Fees: EU students: £2875 f/t; £1440 p/t (provisional)
         Non-EU students: £7650 f/t; 3825 p/t (an additional £500 if taught in one of
                          our overseas centres)

UNIVERSITY OF GLAMORGAN

The Business School
Pontypridd CF37 1DL

T: 01443 483707
F: 01443 482138
E: mrstaylor@glam.ac.uk
W: www.glam.ac.uk

Head of Department: Professor Michael Connolly

CERTIFICATES / DIPLOMAS / MASTER'S DEGREES

■ **PGCert / PGDip / MSc in Educational Management**
Length of course: 1 year f/t; 3 years p/t
Entry requirements: Normally at least a lower second class degree, a teaching qualification and at least two years' experience.
Course content: The MSc is awarded after completion of the following eight modules plus a dissertation; the PGCert after completion of the first four modules; the PGDip after completion of all eight modules.
• Education Environment
• Managing People
• Educational Organisations
• Educational Resource Management (operations)
• Research Methods
• Educational Resource Management (human)
• Management as a Public Policy Process
• *Elective*
Assessment: Coursework
Enquiries: Gerald Dunning; gdunning@glam.ac.uk; T: 01443 482950

■ **MSc in Communicating Science**
Length of course: 1 year f/t
Entry requirements: Normally at least a lower second class degree, a teaching qualification and at least two years' experience.
Course content: The following eight modules plus a dissertation.
• The Public Understanding of Science
• Understanding the Client Group
• How People Learn
• Demonstration Methods
• Communicating Science through Interactive Exhibits
• New Learning Environments
• Research Methods
• Communicating Science in Informal Settings
Assessment: Coursework
Enquiries: Tom Syson; tom@techniquest.org.uk; T: 02920 475475 x246

RESEARCH DEGREES

■ MPhil/PhD

Length of course: *MPhil:* 1.5-3 years f/t; 2.5-4 years p/t
                PhD: 4-6 years f/t; 3-5 years p/t

Entry requirements: Normally at least a lower second class degree, a teaching qualification and at least two years' experience.

Research areas:
• Educational Leadership
• Management & Policy
• Organisational Learning
• Management Learning
• Higher Education Policy & Practice
• Citizenship Education

Assessment: By thesis.

Enquiries: Chirs Laity; claity@glam.ac.uk

Faculty of Education
8 University Gardens
GLASGOW   G12 8QH
Scotland

T: 0141 330 3021
F: 0141 330 5451
E: pgrad@educ.gla.ac.uk
W: www.gla.ac.uk/faculties/education

Change of address from September 2002:
St Andrew's Building
GLASGOW G12 8QQ
Scotland

MASTER'S DEGREES

Length of all Master's courses: 1 year f/t; 2 years p/t

■ MEd in Education

This course is designed to give teachers and other professionals a fuller awareness of their work and its place in the world of scholarship and research.
Entry requirements: Normally a first degree or equivalent and professional training in a field of education or a related profession.
Course content: Core modules are: Modern Educational Thought; Methods of Educational Research; Seminar on Contemporary Issues
Assessment: Ten modules assessed separately, normally by assignment; 15,000-word dissertation; oral examination.

■ MEd in Religious Education

Entry requirements: Normally a first degree or equivalent and professional training in a field of education or a related profession.
Course content:
Compulsory course: Mapping the World of Religion
Optional modules may include: Founding Figures in Christianity; Introduction to Biblical Studies; Hinduism; Islam; Judaism
Double module: Religion, Education and the Classroom
Assessment: Ten modules assessed separately, normally by assignment; 15,000-word dissertation; oral examination.

■ MPhil in Educational Studies

This course is suitable for those with well-developed interest in Education.
Entry requirements: Normally an honours degree or equivalent and career experience.
Course content: *Six modules from a wide choice including:* Theory; Contemporary Issues; Early Childhood Education; Adult Education; Philosophy of Curriculum; Special Education.
Compulosory module: Methods of Educational Research
Assessment: Modules are assessed separately, normally by assignment; 15,000-word dissertation; oral examination.

■ MPhil in Psychology

This degree is recognised by the British Psychological Society as giving the Graduate Basis for Registration.

Entry requirements: Normally an honours degree or equivalent and some relevant experience in Psychology, at least to undergraduate level 1.
Course content: 12 taught modules.
Assessment: Modules assessed individually on the basis of coursework, including research projects and written examination; 15,000-word dissertation.

■ **MSc in Adult and Continuing Education**
Entry requirements: Normally an honours degree or equivalent and career experience.
Course content: Priniciples & Theories; Teaching & Learning; Contemporary Issues; work-based learning placement; Research Methods; choice of specialist option; dissertation.
Assessment: Study units assessed separately, normally by written assignment and presentation; placement assessed by log book and reflective essay; dissertation.

■ **MSc in Science and Science Education**
Entry requirements: Honours degree in science or mathematics; teaching experience desirable.
Course content: Three modules from MEd in Education; one module in Science Education; three modules and associated practical work in specialist subject; training in research methodology; research project in Science Education related to specialist subject.
Assessment: Written examination, coursework and assignments; dissertation on research topic.

RESEARCH DEGREES

■ **MLitt**
Length of course: 2 years f/t; 3 years p/t
Entry requirements: Honours degree of a recognised university; a specific research plan (no professional qualification required).

■ **PhD**
Length of course: 3 years f/t; 4 years p/t
Entry requirements: as MLitt above

■ **PhD (doctoral programme)**
Length of course: 4 years f/t; 5 years p/t
Entry requirements: A degree or equivalent qualification; normally not less than two years' professional experience; a promising initial research topic.

Transfer to and from other degrees:
Students studying for the degree of MEd or the degree of MPhil may be allowed to transfer to the traditional PhD or Doctoral Programme.

FEES: EU students: £2870 f/t; £1435 p/t
Non-EU students: £7500 f/t

UNIVERSITY OF GLOUCESTERSHIRE

Faculty of Education and Social Sciences
Francis Close Hall Campus
Swindon Road
CHELTENHAM   GL50 4AZ

T: 01242 532821
F: 01242 536262

Head of School: Chris Oulton

Formerly Cheltenham & Gloucester College of Higher Education, the University of Gloucestershire came into being on 23 October 2001 and is Britain's newest university. The University has a very diverse programme of academic and vocational higher education.

The University's bases in Cheltenham and Gloucester are situated in a thriving community with a strong local economy, attractive natural environment, historic buildings and diverse and lively cultural background. The area is well served by the nation's network of motorways, coach and rail services, and is almost equidistant from Oxford, Birmingham, Bristol and Cardiff. London is about two hours away.

BACHELOR DEGREES

- **BEd Hons Primary Education (5-11 age range) with QTS**

This course is designed to provide the academic and professional skills required to become an effective primary school teacher and gain the award of QTS. Early Primary (5-8) or Later Primary (7-11) age phase specialisms are offered. All students will study the teaching of English, Maths and Science in depth and be prepared to teach a range of foundation subjects.

Length of course: 3 years

Entry requirements: Maths, English and Science minimum grade C at GCSE or equivalent; at least two A-level passes, including one from English, Maths or Science.

Enquiries: Geoffrey Pryce; gpryce@glos.ac.uk; T: 01242 532764

- **BEd Hons Primary Education (3-8 age range) with QTS**

This course is designed to provide the academic and professional skills required to become an effective primary school teacher and gain the award of QTS. All students will study the teaching of English, Maths and Science in depth. The course provides specialist training in Nursery/KS1.

Length of course: 3 years

Entry requirements: Maths, English and Science minimum grade C at GCSE or equivalent; at least two A-level passes, including English.

Enquiries: Geoffrey Pryce; gpryce@glos.ac.uk; T: 01242 532764

- **BEd Hons Primary Education with QTS** (2-year route)

This course is designed for mature entrants who have satisfactorily completed at least one year of higher education study appropriate as a basis for teaching the primary school curriculum. Students will take modules from the Primary Initial Teacher Training Programme and study alongside students on three-year courses.

Length of course: 2 years

Entry requirements: Maths, English and Science minimum grade C at GCSE or equiva-

lent; at least one year of higher education study in subjects which relate to the National Curriculum.
Enquiries: Geoffrey Pryce; gpryce@glos.ac.uk; T: 01242 532764

CERTIFICATES / DIPLOMAS

■ PGCE Primary
Length of course: 1 year f/t
Entry requirements: Maths and English and a Science subject minimum grade C at GCSE level or equivalent; a degree relevant to the primary curriculum.
Course content: This is a course for graduate students who wish to become primary school teachers. Initial training is offered in the school age ranges 5-8 and 7-11 years. Students are expected to gain a general understanding of good primary practice, as well as specialist knowledge of the needs of the chosen age range. The Postgraduate Certificate is awarded on the basis of satisfactory work in schools and the approved completion of required course work.
Enquiries: Geoffrey Pryce; gpryce@glos.ac.uk; T: 01242 532764
Applications: through the GTTR *(see Glossary)*

■ PGCE Secondary with QTS
Length of course: 1 year f/t
Entry requirements: Maths and English minimum grade C at GCSE level or equivalent; a degree in an area that supports one of the subject specialisms on offer.
Course content: This is a course for graduate students wishing to become secondary school teachers (11 to 18 age range). The subject specialisms on offer:
• Art
• Design Technology
• English
• Geography
• History
• IT
• Maths
• Modern Languages
• Music
• Physical Education
• Religious Education
• Science
Enquiries: *For DT, IT, Music:* Sheila Sykes; ssykes@glos.ac.uk; T: 01452 520594
For all other specialisms: Sue Bongiovanni; sbongiovanni@glos.ac.uk;
T: 01242 532870
Applications: through the GTTR *(see Glossary)*

■ PGCert in Teaching & Learning
This course provides initial professional development for lecturers and professionals involved in education and training. Recognised by the Staff Education and Development Association, the course has national recognition in the Further and Higher Education sectors. The award incorporates the PGCert in Further & Higher Education.
Enquiries: Amanda Pill; apill@glos.ac.uk; T: 01242 543361

MASTER'S DEGREES / CERTIFICATES / DIPLOMAS

- **MEd Professional Development**
- **MEd Educational Leadership**
- **MEd Inclusive Education**
- **PGDip** (in above pathways)
- **PGCert** (in above pathways)

Length of course: 2-5 years p/t; 1 year f/t

Entry requirements: Applicants should normally be qualified graduate or non-graduate teachers who have at least three years' teaching experience in schools or other educational institutions.

Course content: A modular programme. Modules available include:
- Continuing Professional Development
- Methods of Enquiry
- Strategic & Financial Management
- Curriculum Design & Development
- Developing Leadership Skills
- Inclusive Identities
- Mentoring & Coaching
- Learning Difficulties
- Emotional & Behavioural Difficulties

Enquiries: Amanda Pill; apill@glos.ac.uk; T: 01242 543361

RESEARCH DEGREES

- **MPhil, PhD**

Entry requirements: *MPhil:* 1st or 2nd class Honours degree
PhD direct: higher degree
Other PhD candidates: may be admitted to MPhil with transfer to PhD

Research areas:
- Developing Children's Learning
- Educational Identities & Inequalities
- Higher Degree Education
- Management of Children's Behaviour

Fees: EU students: *MPhil:* £3400
PhD direct: £4600
MPhil transferring to PhD: £5400
Non-EU students: £3750 pa

Enquiries: Dr Michael Littledyke; mlittledyke@glos.ac.uk; T: 01242 543414

School of Education & Training

I. Avery Hill Campus
Bexley Road
Eltham
LONDON   SE9 2PQ

II. Maritime Greenwich Campus
Old Royal Naval College
Park Row
LONDON   SE10 9LS

T: 0800 005006
E: courseinfo@greenwich.ac.uk
W: www.gre.ac.uk

Head of School: Dr Mary Stiasny

The School of Education & Training is based at the Avery Hill Campus and in the former Royal Naval College beside the River Thames in the heart of Greenwich. Avery Hill is located in beautiful parkland eight miles south-east of Central London and within easy reach of the airports and the English Channel. The campus has an impressive library, a technology suite, science laboratories, Arts Centre and Lecture Theatres. Overseas students are most welcome and for their study period in the UK have the opportunity to live on campus in a new student village. Many social and cultural activities and sports facilities are available.

At Greenwich, the historic buildings were designed in the 18th century by Sir Christopher Wren, architect of St Paul's Cathedral, as a home for disabled and retired seamen. After sensitive restoration they now provide spacious teaching rooms together with excellent library and ICT facilities. There is a graduate student residence on this campus.

The School has an academic staff of over 100 and provides for education and training awards for practitioners in Primary, Secondary, Further, Adult and Higher Education, together with a suite of degrees in education and community studies and higher degrees including a new professional doctorate. These awards are designed to give flexibility and choice. Both in-service and pre-service education and training are organised within a credit accumulation scheme. Each unit of study has an associated credit rating, thus credit points are awarded after successful completion of a unit. It is also possible to gain accreditation for prior learning (APL) or experiential learning (APEL).

BACHELOR DEGREES

- **BA Hons Education Studies**
This programme does not lead to QTS, but students may be eligible to follow either an employment-based or postgraduate teacher training course in certain circumstances.
Length of course: 3 years f/t; 4-6 years p/t
Entry requirements: Normally university matriculation standard
Course content: The programme of studies comprises both core courses at Levels 1 and 2 (years 1 and 2) together with a variety of options which are undertaken at Level 2 and 3. Two options must be chosen from:
- Early Years Education
- Supporting Curriculum Studies
- Education Management

- Vocational Education
- Intercultural Education
- Special Educational Needs
- *Relevant courses from other Educational & Community Studies degrees by agreement*

Other options may be available - details on request.

Students also undertake a major project in an area of their own choice.

<u>Enquiries:</u> Mr Gavin Farmer

■ BA Hons Education (Steiner Waldorf)

Not recruiting in 2002.

<u>Length of course:</u> 3 years f/t; 4-6 years p/t

<u>Entry requirements:</u> Normally university matriculation standard

<u>Course content:</u> The programme of studies comprises both core courses and specific training for Steiner Waldorf education. It is endorsed by the Steiner Waldorf Schools Federation and designed to lead to teaching in SW schools. Students have the opportunity to follow a subject elective as part of their programme, but the course does not lead to QTS. Periods of practical teaching in SW schools forms part of the programme in each year of the course, and this may include work in schools overseas.

<u>Enquiries:</u> Gavin Farmer

■ BA Hons Childhood Studies

<u>Length of course:</u> 3 years f/t; 4-6 years p/t

<u>Entry requirements:</u> Normally university matriculation standard.

<u>Course content:</u> The programme of studies comprises courses drawn equally from both the Schools of Education & Training and Health & Social Care and students have the opportunity to follow either an early years route or later (adolescent) years route as options at levels 2 and 3. All students undertake a major project as part of their final year.

<u>Enquiries:</u> Ms Liz Gerrish

■ BA Hons Community Arts & Design

This programme does not lead to QTS but suitable students may be eligible to follow a postgraduate teacher training course following graduation.

<u>Length of course:</u> 3 years f/t; 4-6 years p/t

<u>Entry requirements:</u> Normally university matriculation standard

<u>Course content:</u> The programme of studies comprises core courses in a broad range of community arts and design and the opportunity during the latter stages of the degree to follow an option in an area of choice. All students undertake a major personal project based in a community setting as part of their programme in the final year.

<u>Enquiries:</u> Ms Barbara Huish

■ BA Hons Physical Education & Sport

This programme does not lead to QTS but suitable students may be eligible to follow a postgraduate teacher training course following graduation.

<u>Length of course:</u> 3 years f/t; 4-6 years p/t

<u>Entry requirements:</u> Normally university matriculation standard

Course content: The programme of studies initially comprises both core courses in physical education and sport with an opportunity from Level 2 onwards to focus on either a PE route or a Sports route. In the final year students undertake a special project in their chosen route.

Enquiries: Dr Colin Reeves

■ BA Hons Youth & Community Studies

Length of course: 3 years f/t; 4-6 years p/t

Entry requirements: Normally university matriculation standard

Course content: The programme of studies includes both core courses at levels 1 and 2, and the opportunity to focus from Level 2 onwards either in youth studies or community studies. The final year also includes a major project. All students undertake placements as part of the programme, which is designed to lead to qualified professional status. Students can obtain professional recognition on completing stage two of the programme.

Enquiries: Mr Gilbert Browne

■ BA Hons Design Technology Education

Length of course: 3 years f/t; 4-6 years p/t

Entry requirements: Normally university matriculation standard

Course content: The programme of studies is designed to attract students with D&T qualifications to the equivalent of 'A' Level or Advanced GNVQ and wish to extend their understanding of the subject in a community/education context. It is not an initial teacher training course, but suitable graduates may be eligible to embark on a PGCE course. The programme comprises core courses in design, related manufacturing and IT/Computing, with a particular and specific focus on the community. Students follow a variety of core and option subjects and undertake a major personal project.

Enquiries: Mr Ken Webster

■ BA/BSc Hons - Combined Studies

Length of course: 3 years f/t/; 4-6 years p/t

Entry requirements: Normally University matriculation standard

Course content: Education may also be studied as part of the University combined degrees programme either as a joint honours subject or as a major or minor subject combination. A range of combinations are currently available (*others may be available - details on request*):

BA Hons:

- Education & Business
- Education & Child Development
- Education & Economics
- Education & English
- Education & French
- Education & German
- Education & Italian
- Education & Learning Disabilities
- Education & Philosophy

- Education & Politics
- Education & Psychology
- Education & Sociology
- Education & Spanish
- Education & Theology
- Education Science & Society

BA/BSc Hons (major/minor):

- Education with Creative Writing
- Education with Drama
- Education with Fitness Science
- Education with Media Writing
- Education with Religious Studies
- Education with Sports Science
- Health with Education
- Law with Education

BSc Hons:

- Fitness Science & Education
- Health & Education
- Law & Education
- Life Science & Education
- Sports Science & Education

<u>Enquiries:</u> Mr Gavin Farmer

■ BA Hons / BSc Hons with QTS

Details of these primary and secondary initial teacher training courses are available on request.

<u>Enquiries:</u> Andy Hudson; Richard Harris

CERTIFICATES / DIPLOMAS / MASTER'S DEGREES

■ PGCE (PCET) / CertEd (PCET)

This course is franchised to 21 partner colleges in a network of provision.

<u>Length of course</u>: 12 months f/t; 6 years p/t (max); distance learning mode is available.

<u>Entry requirements:</u> Candidates must be qualified in an academic or vocational specialism and have a minimum of 2 years' work experience.

<u>Course content:</u> A wide variety of units is available. Students begin their programme by learning the essentials of planning and assessing teaching. They then move on to use theory to reflect on and improve their practice.

<u>Assessment:</u> Course work and practical teaching.

<u>Enquiries:</u> Ms Anne Cox (FT); Ms Julia Burton (Distance); Ms Lynda Hall (p/t)

■ PGCE Primary and Secondary with QTS

Details of these initial teacher training awards are available on request.

MASTER'S DEGREES

■ **MA Education**

There is a wide choice of units at Master's level, including:

- Curriculum Studies
- Educational Computing
- Educational Management
- Educational Policies & Change
- Language Education
- Maths Education
- Primary Education
- Science Education
- Special Educational Needs
- Technology Education

Depending on the combination of units students may be awarded an 'open' degree or a named award.

Length of course: 12 months f/t; 6 years (max) p/t

Entry requirements: Qualified practitioners in a broad range of educational posts, eg teachers, head-teachers, advisers, inspectors, administrators, counsellors, careers advisers and lecturers.

Assessment: Course work including a research project (total 120 credit points).

Enquiries: Ms Francia Kinchington

RESEARCH DEGREES

■ **MPhil / PhD by research**

Length of course: 2-5 years f/t; 3-6 years p/t

Entry requirements: Educational professionals with an honours degree or a Master's degree in a relevant field to their proposed research.

Research areas:

- Curriculum Studies
- Education Management & Administration
- Gender
- Inter-cultural Education
- Professionalism in FHE
- Science & Technology Education
- Special Educational Needs
- Teaching & Learning in PCET (including the use of ICT)

Assessment: Thesis

OTHER COURSES

■ **Short Courses**

The Schools provide a wide variety of short courses, some of which give credit towards awards. Enquiries are welcome from individuals, schools, colleges and organisations. Short courses can be developed for a school or college and delivered 'in-house'.

Enquiries: Mr Bill Goddard; Ms Harriet Harper

UNIVERSITY OF HERTFORDSHIRE

Department of Education
Watford Campus
Aldenham
WATFORD WD25 8AT

T: 01707 284800
F: 01707 284870
E: admissions@herts.ac.uk
W: www.herts.ac.uk

Enquiries: University Admissions Office, University of Hertfordshire, College Lane, Hatfield AL10 9AB *(telephone, fax, email as above)*

From 2003 these courses will be based on an extensive new purpose-built campus at Hatfield. This will offer international students excellent modern facilities and the benefits of being part of a large student body.

BACHELOR DEGREES

- **BEd/BEd Hons and BA/BA Hons for International Students**
Length of course: 1 year f/t; 2 years f/t for specialised training
Entry requirements: QTS (overseas) with professional experience (overseas).
Course content: Includes Education Studies and Comparative Education.

- **BEd/BEd Hons Primary** (2 or 3 years)

CERTIFICATES / DIPLOMAS / MASTER'S DEGRESS

- **PGCert/PGDip for Teachers of the Hearing Impaired**
Length of course: 1-2 years f/t
Entry requirements: QTS (overseas) with professional experience.
Course content: All aspects of teaching the hearing impaired.

- **PGCE Primary and Secondary** (1 year f/t)

- **PGCert/AdvDip/PGDip/MA/MEd**
Length of course: 1-2 years f/t
Entry requirements: First degree of approved university or recognised teaching quali-fication; at least three years' professional experience in education or a closely related field.
Course content: These up-to-date and relevant courses aim to improve standards of teaching and learning in schools and colleges.

RESEARCH DEGREES

- **MPhil/PhD**
- **MRes**
Length of course: *MPhil, PhD:* 3-6 years f/t or p/t
               MRes: 1 year f/t
Entry requirements: Good first degree and post-experience qualifications. Enquirers should provide details of their proposed research area.
Research areas: Literacy; Early Childhood Education; Applied Linguistics; Special Edu-cation (including Autism and Hearing Impairment); Equality; Teaching; Learning; Cur-riculum.

The School of Education & Professional Development
Queensgate
HUDDERSFIELD   HD1 3DH

T: 01484 478270
F: 01484 478231
E: a.shaw2@hud.ac.uk
W: www.hud.ac.uk

<u>Dean of School:</u> Freda Bridge

BACHELOR DEGREES

■ BEd / BEd Hons

This is a specially designed pathway within the university's credit accumulation scheme for experienced teachers and managers of vocational subjects working in a developing country context. There are flexible entry and study patterns and success on the pathway enables people to progress to more advanced qualifications.

<u>Length of course:</u> There are three main patterns of attendance depending on qualifications at entry:

- 21 months starting September - incorporating an industrial attachment in the summer.
- 12 months starting June - incorporating an industrial attachment in the summer.

In the above two modes it is possible to accumulate sufficient credit for the degree to be awarded with honours.

- 9 months starting September - this route is for teachers with substantial professional experience and leads to an unclassified degree.

<u>Entry requirements:</u> Appropriate qualification (obtained by examination) for the specialist subject taught (eg HND or Certificate, BTEC, CGLI); normally at least two years' teaching experience.

<u>Course content:</u>

Year 1 (Certificate in Education)

Core modules are provided in each of the following role areas:

- Teacher as Planner, Designer of Learning, Assessor
- Teacher as Practitioner (including teaching practice)
- Teacher as Curriculum Developer

Other modules will be chosen from:

- Teacher as Subject Specialist
- Teacher as Facilitator
- Teacher as Evaluator
- Teacher as Enterpriser
- Teacher as Professional

Year 2

- Industrial/Commercial Placement (Hons only)
- Curriculum Perspectives
- Curriculum Planning & Design
- Information Technology
- Programme Planning
- Educational Enquiry
- Educational Technology
- Issues in Development Education

- Curriculum Management
- Professional Experience (college placement)
- Subject-based Study (Hons only)
- Subject-based Curriculum Study (Hons only)
- Synoptic Study

MASTER'S DEGREES

■ MA Education (Human Resource Development)

Length of course: 12 months f/t (normally commencing in mid-September, but a January start is also available); 24 months p/t (including off-campus delivery)

Entry requirements: Normally a recognised first degree in a professional area (eg BEd) or a first degree together with, where appropriate, a recognised professional qualification; normally at least two years' full-time experience in an appropriate professional area.

Course content: 120 credits at 'M' level are required for this degree. Fifty of these are accumulated through the following three modules which form the foundation for further study (30) and a dissertation which enables participants to investigate in-depth an issue of professional concern (40):

- *Concepts, Problems & Analysis* (20 credits): Enables students working in education and related areas to develop systematic problem solving skills, to recommend appropriate strategies of investigation and to propose constructive solutions to problems. The module incorporates philosophical considerations relating to education and development.
- *Educational Research Methodology* (10 credits): Prepares students for systematic, in-depth investigation into educational and other related areas of concern.
- *Education, Society & Development* (20 credits): Studies the processes of policy formation and implementation within the economic, social and political constraints of development.

The remaining 30 credits are normally made up from the following modules, but it may be possible to negotiate alternatives:

- *Management of Education in a Development Context* (20 credits): Is concerned with issues relating to the effective management of change in education and training.
- *Introduction to Human Resource Development* (10 credits): Studies the identification and possible approaches to meeting human resource development needs.

Assessment: Modules are assessed by assignment work; there are no examinations.

RESEARCH DEGREES

■ MPhil, PhD

These research programmes are offered on a full- or part-time basis.

Entry requirements: Normally a degree of the CNAA, a degree of a university in the UK or an equivalent qualification from an overseas institution.

Course content/structure: Candidates are required to undertake a critical study of a selected topic or topics which involves original and detailed research, evaluation and analysis of appropriate secondary sources and will be presented in the form of a written dissertation. In addition, students may be required to attend lectures in post-graduate or honours degree pathways, study groups and workshops, as well as participating in seminars, colloquia and conferences.

Normally two supervisors will be appointed to assist and advise candidates on their study programme and research activities. One supervisor will be the Director of Studies (normally a member of the University) with responsibility to supervise the candidate on a regular basis. The second supervisor may be appointed from the University or from elsewhere (eg from the candidate's employing institution).

For part-time students who are not normally resident in the UK a suitable local supervisor may be appointed by the University for the purpose of providing regular guidance. However, the Director of Studies will be required to meet the candidate periodically, in accordance with an approved timetable for such meetings.

Research students may be accepted to undertake research on any topic which falls within the areas of activity of the School of Education. However, the following fields of research are of particular interest to the School:

- All aspects of technical and vocational education in developing countries
- Course management in FHE
- Curriculum evaluation for pre-vocational courses
- Professional accountability in FHE
- The maintenance and improvement of standards in FHE
- Inequalities in educational provision (including provision for women and ethnic minorities in FHE)
- Open learning in FHE
- Strategies for implementing national/local government educational policies in FHE
- Self-assessment in FHE

OTHER COURSES

■ Fellowships

The International Development Centre organises fellowship attachments for both UK and overseas education and training specialists. These fellowships provide the opportunity for personal research in collaboration with academic staff in the School. Each programme is individually designed to meet the specific needs of the Fellow.

Length of courses: normally 2-3 months

UNIVERSITY OF HULL

Institute for Learning
Cottingham Road
HULL HU6 7RX

T: 01482 465406
F: 01482 466133
E: j.henderson@hull.ac.uk
W: www.hull.ac.uk/ifl/ifl

Director: Professor Graham Chesters
Enquiries: The Advanced Programmes Admissions Secretary

The University of Hull offers courses and research facilities in advanced educational study for the following qualifications:
Research Degrees: PhD (normally 3 calendar years)
EdD (normally 3 calendar years)
MPhil (normally 2 calendar years)
MEd (1 calendar year)
Taught Courses: MEd (1 calendar year)
Details of the courses leading to these qualifications are as follows:

CERTIFICATES / DIPLOMAS

■ PGCE Primary and Secondary with QTS
Length of course: 1 academic year
Entry requirements: Degree plus GCSE or equivalent requirements in English and Maths.
Course content:
• Biology
• Business Studies
• Chemistry
• Citizenship
• English
• Geography
• History
• Maths
• Modern Languages
• Physics
• RE
Enquiries: Christopher Brown

MASTER'S DEGREES

■ MEd
Length of course: 1 calendar year
Entry requirements: Honours degree and teaching certificate or teaching certificate and Advanced Diploma or equivalent qualifications and experience in the field of training.
Course content: Candidates will select six modules (three in each of the two semesters) from a range of titles available. Modules have been designed to cater for the interests of Primary and Secondary School teachers, lecturers and those involved in

Glossary on page XI

post-school education training and development, educational administrators and researchers and other related areas.

Assessment: A combination of course work assignments amounting to a total of 3000 to 4000 words per module and a dissertation of up to 20,000 words on a topic related to the modules studied.

Enquiries: Ian Shaw

RESEARCH DEGREES

■ MEd by research, MPhil, PhD

Length of course:

PhD: Normally 3 calendar years, but may be reduced to 2 years for those who already hold a Master's degree.

MPhil: Normally 2 calendar years.

MEd: Normally 1 calendar year.

Course content: Supervision is provided for research in most areas of primary and secondary education as well as research in:

• Post-school Education
• Training & Development
• Vocational Education & Training
• Higher Education & Adult Education
• Educational Administration
• Continuing Professional Development

Assessment: Thesis

Enquiries: Professor Michael P Bottery

■ EdD (taught doctorate)

Programme director: Prof Michael P Bottery

Length of course: Normally 3 years

Entry requirements: Master's degree.

Course content: Candidates will select six modules from a choice of nine plus two further modules in the area of educational research and enquiry.

Assessment: Course work assignments and a thesis of up to 50,000 words.

FEES: EU students (excluding PGCE): £2810 pa
EU students (PGCE): no fees
Non-EU students: £6750 pa

RESIDENCE FEES: Fees range from £1781 for a shared room in a self-catering student house to £3216 for a single room with en-suite facilities.

KEELE UNIVERSITY

Department of Education
KEELE ST5 5BG

T: 01782 583114
F: 01782 583555
W: www.keele.ac.uk/depts/ed/educ2.htm

Head of Department: Dr Ken Jones
Prospectus: Postgraduate Admission, Department of Academic Affairs

The Keele Department of Education is a major provider of initial secondary teacher education, both at undergraduate and at postgraduate level. We cooperate closely with local schools. Through curriculum development projects and support for action research we work with schools to develop their capacities. Our MA, MBA and EdD programmes support and inform theoretically the reflective activity of education professionals. Through research in education as social policy, we aim to analyse and provoke discussion about current patterns of educational change.

Our goal is to integrate our teaching and our support for the work of schools with research that addresses central contemporary issues in education - in Britain and, increasingly, in Europe.

BACHELOR DEGREES

- **BA / BSc in Educational Studies**

Length of course: 3 years

Entry requirements: 3 A-levels or equivalent.

Course content: Educational Studies is a subject offered within Keele's dual honours degree programme and must be taken in combination with another subject to be chosen from a range of arts, social studies and science subjects. It combines in-depth academic study with work that has an applied and vocational orientation. It draws on philosophy, sociology, politics, psychology and economics and links the study of education to social policy, childhood, culture and information and communication technology. The course seeks to prepare students for a range of professional careers involving, or allied to, education and training. Though it does not, in itself, provide QTS, it is excellent preparation for PGCE courses and we may be able to offer a guaranteed place on the PGCE Secondary Course at Keele (subject to specific conditions).

Enquiries: Tracy Roberts; eda41@keele.ac.uk; T: 01782 582125

CERTIFICATES / DIPLOMAS / MASTER'S DEGREES

- **Certificate/Diploma , MA in Effective Education & Management**

Length of course: Diploma/MA: 2 years p/t
                  Certificate: ca 6 months

Entry requirements: Normally 1st or 2nd class honours degree in an appropriate subject plus two year's professional experience.

Course content: The course is aimed at qualified teachers involved in/aspiring to management in schools, colleges, FE/HE and related agencies. The MA course comprises a range of taught modules (number/range taken depends on qualification) plus dissertation and uses seminars/tutorials and lectures plus self-supported study (open/ flexible learning materials). Course modules include:

- Effective Management
- Improving Professional Practice
- Effective Teaching
- Independent Action Research Report
- Effective Learning & Assessment
- Policy for Improvement
- Professional Development Needs Analysis
- Research Methods
- Dissertation

Assessment: Coursework assignments and dissertation.
Enquiries / Fees: Dorothy Tyson; eda04@keele.ac.uk; T: 01782 583126

■ **Certificate/Diploma , MBA Education**
Length of course: *MBA:* 2 years p/t
Certificate/Diploma: 10-18 months
Entry requirements: There are no specific undergraduate subject requirements, but students should have a good honours degree to commence the course at Master's level. Some students enter with accreditation for prior learning and/or alternative prior educational experience.
Course content: The course is structured for managers and aspiring managers in education and related public-private sector organisations (eg LEAs, universities, colleges, schools, training agencies, NHS). The course comprises six taught modules and a dissertation. Students meet for two consecutive days in each of the first five terms of the course. Course modules include:
- Organisational Behaviour
- Quality, Improvement and Effectiveness
- Strategic Management
- Human Resource Issues
- Resource Management
- Research Methods
- Dissertation

Assessment: Coursework assignments and dissertation.
Enquiries / Fees: Dorothy Tyson; eda04@keele.ac.uk; T: 01782 583126

RESEARCH DEGREES

■ **MPhil by research, PhD**
Entry requirements: *MPhil:* 1st or 2nd honours degree
PhD: Normally higher degree, but candidates may initially be admitted to MPhil programme and transfer to PhD.
Supervision is offered in a wide range of areas of education, including:
- Sociology
- Psychology & Philosophy of Education
- Gender, Family (Parents and/or Children) & Education
- Evidence-informed Policy & Practitioner Research
- Education Policy & Practice

- Education Management (including FE & HE)
- Professional Development

Enquiries / Fees: Gladys Pye; eda32@keele.ac.uk; T: 01782 583129

■ **EdD: Evidence-informed Education Policy-making & Practice (EPP) and Gender & Education Management (GEM)**

Length of courses: 4 years p/t (2 years of residential modules and an organisational work ethnography); 2 years for a 50,000-word (min) thesis

Entry requirements: A Master's degree of this university or another deemed equivalent, normally in the general field of education, policy and/or management and/or social sciences or its equivalent in professional experience and a professionally accredited programme.

Course content: These programmes combine advanced studies in short residential modules in either policy and practitioner research or gender and education management with research methods in preparation for the thesis research proposal and thesis itself

Enquiries / Fees: Amanda Mobberley; eda29@keele.ac.uk; T: 01782 584436

OTHER COURSES

The modules in the Certificate/Diploma and MA programme are offered as short courses (single or paired).

Length of courses: 3-4 months

Enquiries / Fees: Dorothy Tyson; eda04@keele.ac.uk; T: 01782 583126

School of Education
WINCHESTER SO22 4NR

T: 01962 827348
F:01962 827479
W: www.wkac.ac.uk

Head of School: Professor Anne Williams
Enquiries: Paula Moorse; p.moorse@wkac.ac.uk

CERTIFICATES / DIPLOMAS

■ **Diploma in Advanced Educational Studies**
This course is designed for experienced teachers in schools wishing to obtain an advanced qualification.
Length of course: 9 months f/t
Entry requirements: Open to graduates and suitably qualified non-graduates.
Course content: Candidates will be assessed on modules which cover primary or secondary policy and practice, aspects of the curriculum, teaching and learning and research of classroom practice. Modules negotiable with School of Education tutors.
Assessment: Through course work.
This Diploma is an access route to the MA in Education (see below).

MASTER'S DEGREES

■ **MA in Education: Professional Enquiry**
Length of course: 1 year f/t
Entry requirements: Open to graduates and suitably qualified non-graduates.
Course content: This course combines advanced study with undertaking of projects related to professional needs and concerns. The modules cover primary or secondary policy and practice, aspects of the curriculum, teaching and learning and research of classroom practice. Modules negotiable with School of Education tutors.
Assessment: Through course work.
The Diploma in Advanced Educational Studies (see above) is an access route to this MA.

RESEARCH DEGREES

■ **MPhil, PhD**
Length of course: MPhil: 1 year f/t; PhD: 3 years f/t
Entry requirements: Open to graduates and suitably qualified non-graduates.
Research areas: Supervision is available for education related projects including nursery, primary, secondary and teacher education.
Assessment: Through course work.

FEES: *on request*

LANCASTER UNIVERSITY

Department of Educational Research
LANCASTER LA1 4YL

T: 01524 593189
F:01524 592914
E: j.gomersall@lancaster.ac.uk
W: www.lancs.ac.uk/depts/edres/index.htm

<u>Head of Department:</u> Dr Colin Rogers

BACHELOR DEGREES

- **BA in Educational Studies**
- **BA in Educational Research**
- **BSc in Education & Psychology**

<u>Length of courses:</u> 3 years f/t
<u>Entry requirements:</u> *BAs:* 3 subjects at A-level grades CCC or equivalent.
BSc: 3 subjects at A-level grades BBC or equivalent; GCSE Maths.
<u>Fees:</u> EU students: £1075 pa f/t
        Non-EU students: £7290 pa f/t
<u>Enquiries:</u> E: j.gomersall@lancaster.ac.uk

DIPLOMAS / MASTER'S DEGREES

The Department has a broad portfolio of postgraduate studies designed to provide Academic and Continuing Professional Development for teachers, educationalists and others concerned with learning and learning technology.

- **MA in Education**
- **MA in Educational Research**

<u>Length of courses:</u> 1 year f/t; 2-4 years p/t
<u>Entry requirements:</u> Good honours degree or equivalent.
<u>Fees:</u> EU students: £2805 pa f/t
        Non-EU students: £7290 pa f/t
<u>Enquiries:</u> E: edres-ma@lancaster.ac.uk

- **MSc/Diploma in Advanced Learning Technology**
- **MSc/Diploma in Networked Learning**
- **MSc/Diploma in Multimedia Courseware Engineering**

<u>Length of courses:</u> 2-4 years p/t (3 months per module)
<u>Entry requirements:</u> Good honours degree or equivalent.
<u>Fees:</u> MSc: £4790
        Diploma: £4120
        Stand-alone module: £745
<u>Enquiries:</u> E: csalt@lancaster.ac.uk; see also: http://csalt.lancs.ac.uk/alt

RESEARCH DEGREES

■ **PhD**

The Department offers a wide range of supervision opportunities including the following areas:

- Adult Education
- Assessment
- Curriculum Implementation
- Language & Literacy
- Psychology of Education
- Women & Education
- Educational Management
- Policy & Organisation
- Advanced Learning Technology

<u>Length of course:</u> 3 years f/t; 5 years p/t

<u>Entry requirements:</u> Good honours degree or equivalent.

<u>Assessment:</u> One year research training; submission of 100,000-word (max) thesis (normally after two or more years).

<u>Fees:</u> EU students: £2805 pa f/t
      Non-EU students: £7290 pa f/t

<u>Enquiries:</u> E: edresearch@lancaster.ac.uk

School of Education
LEEDS LS2 9JT

T: 0113 343 4545
F: 0113 343 4541
E: inter@education.leeds.ac.uk
W: www.education.leeds.ac.uk

The School of Education in the University of Leeds offers a wide range of courses which are suitable for students from overseas. Courses are provided in the following categories:
• Undergraduate single and joint honours programmes.
• A Postgraduate Certificate in Education which is an initial teaching qualification for primary or secondary schools.
• Graduate diplomas and certificates for experienced and qualified educationists in a range of specialisms including programmes developed particularly for overseas education.
• Both specialised and general MEd programmes including taught courses with an overseas orientation.
• Tailor-made MEd programmes taught in-country for specific funders, eg part-time MEd programmes in: Primary Education (Hungary), Professional Development and Basic/Primary Education in Developing Countries (Kenya), General MEd (Norway).
• Higher degrees by research (MEd, MPhil, PhD)
• Taught doctorates (EdD)
• Short courses and attachments designed specifically to meet particular needs of overseas educationists.
Each of these is detailed below.

BACHELOR DEGREES

■ **BA Hons Childhood Studies**
Length of course: 3 years f/t; 5-6 years p/t
Entry requirements: A validated Access Course certificate *or* 3 passes in the A-Level examination (BTEC, Advanced GNVQ/AVCE or NNEB equivalence may be counted to-wards required A-Level passes) *or* 2 A-levels with 2 AS passes *or* an Open University Foundation credit *or* entry through the University of Leeds mature entry scheme *or* equivalent.
Course content: This course offers academic study in the field of childhood education and care, sociology/social policy and psychology, and provides a qualification de-signed for those wishing for professional or personal reasons to develop knowledge and skills in the fields of policy, health, education and the care of young children and their families. Students will be able to achieve this through the study of core educa-tion modules and inter-disciplinary modules in Childhood Studies.
The degree is designed to meet the increasing demands for well qualified early years specialists able to work with young children and their families, both in the community and in the institutions which meet their needs. It will draw on the strengths of the staff within the School of Education and other departments in the University to pro-vide relevant grounding in the fields of social policy, education, care and health.
The degree offers modules in education, health, sociology/social policy and psychol-ogy and has a strong vocational element to help students orientate themselves to-

wards a career. By developing a sound academic base for the analysis and development of practice, the degree will produce professionals who are equipped to deal with the rapid changes that are a feature of this complex area of policy and provision for children and their families.

Fees: _EU students:_ £1100; _Non-EU students:_ £7124
Applications: UCAS _(see Glossary)_
Enquiries: Undergraduate Office; undergrad@education.leeds.ac.uk; T: 0113 343 4671

- **BA Education-French**
- **BA Education-German**
- **BA Education-Spanish**
- **BA Education-Geography**
- **BA Education-Maths**
- **BA Education-Music**
- **BA Education-Sociology**
- **BA Education-Social Policy**
- **BA Education-Politics**
- **BSc Education-Geography**
- **BSc Education-Maths**

Length of course: 3 or 4 years (for Education-French/German/Spanish) f/t
Entry requirements: 3 good passes at A-level with a B in the specialist subject
Course content: Level 1 of the Education component will provide students with an introduction to learning processes, to teaching and practice in the classroom, to models of schooling within the UK and other less formal learning contexts. Education levels 2 and 3 build on level 1 foundation work, looking in greater detail at _Contemporary Issues_ such as:
- Gender issues
- Influences of class, poverty and dis/advantage in schools and society
- Diversity
- The origins and development of concepts of culture
- Influence of the media on educational priorities
- Commercial and industrial influences
- Information and Communications Technology

In _Using and Doing Research_ students will be introduced to the theoretical and applied aspects of educational and social research. As an integral part of the module, students will be able to apply these techniques in a chosen field setting such as a school, social services or commercial office as part of a micro-study.

The subject specialism application module gives students the opportunity to look at their own subject within the context of Education provided by the other modules.

An in-depth study combines the subject specialism with some aspect of Education and builds on the experience of the Research in Education modules.

Further information on the French/German/Spanish, Geography, Maths and Music components (as well as Education) is available from the contact details below.

Fees: Combined Arts: _EU students:_ £1100; _Non-EU students:_ £7124
    Combined Arts/Science: _EU students:_ £1490; _Non-EU students:_ £8289
Applications: UCAS _(see Glossary)_

Glossary on page XI

Education-French/German/Spanish: Centre for Joint Honours in Modern Languages; m.a.nettleton@leeds.ac.uk; T: 0113 343 2700; F: 0113 343 2699

Education-Geography/Maths/Music/Sociology/Social Policy/Politics: Centre for Joint Honours in Arts and Social Sciences; d.aston@leeds.ac.uk; T: 0113 343 3535; F: 0113 343 3533

BSc Education-Geography/Maths: Centre for Joint Honours, Division of Science; c.a.coulson@leeds.ac.uk; T: 0113 343 2691; F: 0113 343 2689

- **BA Joint Honours French & TESOL**
- **BA Joint Honours German & TESOL**
- **BA Joint Honours Spanish & TESOL**
- **BA Joint Honours Portuguese & TESOL**

<u>Length of course</u>: 4 years f/t, including a year abroad

<u>Entry requirements</u>: 3 good passes at A-level

<u>Course content</u>: By the end of this programme, students should be able to combine practical and theoretical knowledge of French or German or Spanish or Portuguese language and culture with an understanding of the processes of teaching English as a second language. They should develop a high level of performance skills in their language of choice, knowledge of significant aspects of French or German or Spanish or Portuguese culture, knowledge of the structures and patterns of current English usage, relevant to language teaching and knowledge of the processes of second/foreign language learning and teaching.

<u>Fees:</u> *EU students:* £1100; *Non-EU students:* £7124

<u>Applications</u>: UCAS (*see Glossary*)

<u>Enquiries:</u> Centre for Joint Honours in Modern Languages; m.a.nettleton@leeds.ac.uk; T: 0113 343 2700; F: 0113 343 2699

CERTIFICATES / DIPLOMAS

- **PGCE Primary and Secondary**

<u>Length of course:</u> from mid-September to early July the following year

<u>Entry requirements:</u> A first degree and GCSE grade C Maths and English (and Science for Primary) or equivalent. For the Secondary course the degree subject must be in one of the following areas which are offered as first teaching subjects:

• Art & Design	• English	• Maths
• Biology	• French	• Music
• Chemistry	• German	• RE
• D&T	• History	• Social Science
• Drama	• IT	• Spanish

Students must have an excellent command of English as much of the course is school-based.

<u>Course content:</u> The primary course is designed to train general class teachers at primary level and students study a range of subjects. Primary students also study for a specialist role. Both the primary and secondary courses are suitable for some overseas students, particularly those who have graduated in the UK but others are welcome to apply.

The qualification of PGCE does not in itself entitle an overseas student to teach outside the UK. Prospective students should make sure that the qualification is acceptable as a teaching qualification in their own country.

Fees: *EU students:* £1100; *Non-EU students:* £7124
Enquiries and application forms: Admissions, ITT Office; pgce@education.leeds.ac.uk;
T: 0113 343 4523

MASTER'S DEGREES

■ MEd - General Programme

The MEd degree is a modular scheme which has been carefully designed to meet the needs of practising schoolteachers, lecturers, administrators and those involved in education.

Length of course: 12 months f/t; 24 months p/t

The course usually begins in October, though a February start is possible. It may be possible to complete certain elements of the course with distance supervision though students must spend at least one whole semester studying full-time at the University of Leeds from the middle to late September to the beginning of February.

Entry requirements: Normally a first degree and at least 2 years' experience of teaching or other approved work.

Course content: Students normally take four taught modules and write a Critical Study (weighted 2 modules). There are some 80 modules within the General MEd in Education scheme. The extensive list of modules includes the general areas of:

- Primary Education
- Most National Curriculum subjects
- Lifelong Learning
- TESOL
- International Educational Management & Administration
- Curriculum Development & Evaluation
- Assessment
- Teaching & Learning
- Educational Psychology & Child Development
- IT & Multimedia
- Current Issues in Education
- Educational Research Methods

Assessment: Course work and dissertation (students are not required to sit examination papers).

*In addition to the General MEd programme (see above), a number of **specialised MEd programmes** are offered. These aim to meet the needs of those with experience or professional interest in the specialist areas and who are seeking to develop their knowledge, skills and expertise. The programmes attract teachers, advisers, curriculum developers, teacher trainers and administrators from all over the world. The specialised MEd courses follow the pattern described above in the General MEd in Education programme.*

Outline descriptions of the specialised programmes are given below. Students may choose to follow all four taught modules in their specialist area or there may be the possibility of selecting one module from another specialist area or from those available in the General MEd programme.

Unless otherwise indicated, the following information applies to all specialised MEd courses:

Glossary on page XI

Fees: *EU students:* £2900 f/t, £858 p/t; *Non-EU students:* £7124 f/t, £3562 p/t
Enquiries and application forms: Higher Degrees and Professional Development Office; med@education.leeds.ac.uk; T: 0113 343 4690/4528; F: 0113 343 4541
Application should be made by May for entry in October.

- **MEd in IT, Multimedia & Education (also by distance learning)**
This course is appropriate for those with current or prospective interests or responsibility relating to IT and multimedia applications in schools and further and higher education. In addition to those with specific commitments to using IT and multimedia, the programme will also be relevant to those seeking to develop an understanding of issues raised by the new technologies in society and the implications for educational curricula and teaching/learning methods. Previous experience with computers or multimedia is neither expected nor required. The emphasis of the programme will not be placed on technical details but on principles, techniques and effects of the technologies on communication, interaction and collaborative learning and problem-solving.

- **MEd in International Educational Management**
This specialised programme is suitable for experienced teachers and officials from abroad with current or prospective management responsibilities in schools, and for governors, ministry officials and students of development. The programme will particularly, but by no means exclusively, focus on less industrialised countries. The aims of this specialist MEd are: to provide an intellectually challenging and professionally relevant programme; to develop participants' skills in management, especially those of policy-making and planning; to enable participants to plan and run effective schools; to enable participants to compare how educational management works in many different countries; and to encourage the participation of individual participants in the programme.

- **MEd in Lifelong Learning**
This programme is offered by the School of Continuing Education in co-operation with the School of Education. The programme is targeted at the wide range of organisations and occupations making significant contributions to lifelong learning, in addition to colleges and universities; for example: employers, libraries, health education, guidance and learning support, training and development, trade unions, voluntary organisations. The programme will provide professionals working in these different areas with the opportunity to learn how to: demonstrate an understanding of different interpretations of lifelong learning and related policy developments; use research on lifelong learning and post-compulsory education and training to inform their own practice; reflect critically on changes experienced in their professional life and in the post-compulsory education and training sectors; use critical, analytical and research skills in a lifelong learning professional context.
Entry requirements: Normally two years professional experience in a field of lifelong learning.

- **MEd in Maths Education**
This programme has been designed for professionals working at all levels in Maths education and is particularly suitable for international students. It has a broad base which allows for many specialisms to develop. It addresses primary, secondary and

higher level Maths education. This specialism covers learning and teaching Maths as well as curriculum, assessment and research issues. It is informed by and addresses national and international developments, issues and research in Maths education. The programme addresses the challenges faced by teachers, teacher-educators and advisors/inspectors and aims to provide opportunities for the study of the whole range of Maths education and to produce better informed and better qualified Maths educators.

■ **MEd in Primary Education**
This programme is designed for experienced primary teachers and headteachers, and other professionals involved in the education of children aged 3-13. The programme is designed to ensure that participants are enabled: to develop their understanding of generic issues related to the primary curriculum, specialist teaching in primary schools and the role of subject knowledge; to enhance their subject knowledge in two or more areas, including at least one core subject or the early years phase; and to undertake school-based work which will inform and support specialist teaching including numeracy and/or literacy.

■ **MEd in Religious Education**
This programme is offered by the Department of Theology and Religious Studies in cooperation with the School of Education. This arrangement enables the bringing together of the teaching and research staff of a department at the forefront of studying Theology and Religious Studies and of an internationally renowned School of Education. The course is appropriate for teachers with current or prospective responsibility for curriculum leadership in RE. It will also be relevant to those seeking to further their understanding of RE and of teaching and learning in this subject area. On completion of this programme, participants will have: learned critically to assess syllabus requirements; developed a firmer grasp of syllabus content; practised and reflected on methods of study in the fields of Theology and RE; assessed a wide range of resources; reflected on ways of approaching religions and related issues in a classroom; and extended and deepened their competence in specific areas of Theology or Religious Studies.

■ **MEd in Science Education**
This programme has been designed to meet the needs of professionals working at all levels in science education and is particularly suitable for international students. It has a broad base which allows for many specialisms to develop. It addresses both primary and secondary science education. It covers learning and teaching science, curriculum, assessment and research issues, as well as issues relating to science education in developing countries. It is informed by and addresses national and international developments, issues and research in science education. The programme addresses the challenges faced by teachers, teacher-educators and advisors/inspectors concerned with science education. It aims to provide opportunities for the study of the whole range of science education and to produce better-informed and better-qualified science educators.

■ **MEd in SEN**
This programme aims to meet the needs of professionals involved in the broad area of special education. The course is intended for teachers, lecturers, administrators and

other professionals in special education from the international community who wish to advance their careers and enhance their knowledge. The central concern of the programme is to promote effective educational practice for pupils with special educational needs (SEN), through increasing teacher expectations: their knowledge of current legislation, reports and relevant research; their understanding of the nature of SEN and of strategies which may best support the learning and achievement of pupils, including collaborative partnerships with others - pupils, parents, colleagues, support assistants and external support agencies. An emphasis is placed on participants' professional knowledge and understanding of current research evidence and its implications for the development of classroom/school-wide strategies which will best support pupils' learning and achievements.

■ **MEd in TESOL**

This programme is designed for those involved in the teaching of English to speakers of other languages. It is appropriate for both native and non-native speakers. Participants' professional backgrounds include: school teachers, teacher trainers, language school directors, curriculum developers, inspectors, university or college lecturers, and materials writers. The course is not suitable for those without professional experience. The overall aims of the programme are: to provide students with an in-depth understanding and critical appreciation of theory and practice in the field of TESOL; to provide opportunities for students to reflect on their own professional experience and practice in the light of their current studies; to provide opportunities for participants to follow their specialist interests; and to enable students to leave the programme in a position to initiate action and to lead development.

Entry requirements: Normally a first degree, a professional qualification and at least three years' relevant experience.

■ **MEd in TESOL for Young Learners**

This programme is designed for teachers, trainers, curriculum specialists, textbook writers and others who are concerned with teaching English to young learners. It offers an excellent opportunity both to those who wish to gain a sound introduction to this specialist area of TESOL teaching for career purposes, and to those who wish to build on their own experience of teaching young learners by exploring or researching particular aspects of this area in-depth. The main aims of the programme are: to provide students with an in-depth understanding and critical appreciation of theory and practice in the field; to provide opportunities for them to reflect on their own professional experience and practice in the light of their current studies; to develop their ability to use a range of analytical tools/procedures to carry out analyses of policies, curricula, teaching/learning materials and empirical investigations; to provide opportunities for participants to follow their specialist interests in teacher training, testing, syllabus and materials design for young learners.

■ **MEd TESOL by distance learning**

This programme is principally aimed at those living overseas who wish to obtain a Master's level qualification but are unable to spend a full academic year away from home.

Length of course: 2 (min) - 5 (max) years

There are two entry points each year: September and April (subject to numbers).

Applications for September entry are possible right up to the beginning of September and for April entry until the end of February. Early application ensures maximum study time.

Entry requirements: The programme is suitable for both native and non-native speakers. Candidates must:

- have a first degree or initial teaching qualification, five years' experience, IELTS 6.5 or TOEFL 610 or computer TOEFL 253 or more with a score of 4 in the writing paper.
- have easy access to email, WWW and a reliable postal service.
- be working in the TESOL profession in some capacity (for e.g. teacher, teacher trainer, language school director, curriculum developer, advisor, inspector, materials writer, university or college lecturer).

Course content/structure:

The course aims to:

- introduce students to current debates in the main areas of TESOL and to examine how these connect to and affect other areas of the profession.
- to help students develop their ability to examine, describe and interpret data from their working environment in the light of such ideas in ways that are appropriate to their context.
- to develop their capacity to make informed and appropriate decisions for professional action in their own TESOL context and in the wider professional community.

Time in Leeds: Students spend the first three months of the programme on a non-assessed, but strongly recommended, study skills module. Following this module, students choose to spend another one (minimum) to six months (maximum) at Leeds. For each of the two face-to-face modules at Leeds, a materials pack will be provided.

Distance learning: Full support systems have been established to enable contact between participants and the distance administrator, module convenors and programme co-ordinator at Leeds - by telephone, fax and email. Study materials for the distance modules are provided. Participants exchange ideas with fellow students via web-based tasks.

Fees: *EU students:* £2900; *Non-EU students:* £6100 (payable in 4 instalments)

Enquiries and details: See www.education.leeds.ac.uk/masters/tesol-dl.htm or contact the Higher Degrees & Professional Development Office.

RESEARCH DEGREES

MEd by research, EdD, MPhil, PhD

The School of Education is one of the largest in the UK and consistently receives a high research rating in the Universities Research Assessment Exercise.

Length of course: *MEd by research:* 1 year f/t; 2 years p/t
                 MPhil: 2-3(max) years f/t ; 3-4(max) years p/t
                 PhD/EdD: 3-4(max) years f/t; 5-7(max) years p/t

Entry requirements: Normally a good first degree or a Master's degree in a subject related to the proposed research topic.

Course content: These degrees involve the preparation of a thesis under the supervision of one or more members of staff. Students attend research methods courses to deepen their research skills and a range of other courses.

The EdD is studied partly through taught modules and partly through the preparation of a thesis under the guidance of a supervisor. Modules are provided in a range of specialisms and also in research methods.

Research areas: Members of staff have a strong research record and interests in:
• Mathematical Education
• Science Education
• Modern Languages Education
• TESOL
• Curriculum Studies (age- or subject-related)
• SEN
• IT, Multimedia & Education
• Educational Management & Administration
• Primary Education
• Lifelong Learning
• Teacher Education & Mentoring

Special Overseas Scheme: PhD students from overseas can have a split location arrangement whereby up to 12 months' fieldwork is conducted in their own country as part of their degree. Some part-time/full-time arrangements are also possible, involving periods of part-time study in the home country and periods of full-time study in Leeds.

Fees: *EU students:* £2950 f/t, £958 p/t; *Non-EU students:* £7124 f/t, £3562 split-site

Enquiries and application forms: Higher Degrees & Professional Development Office; research@education.leeds.ac.uk; T: 0113 343 4527; F: 0113 343 4541

OTHER COURSES

■ Short Courses

The School of Education offers facilities for specially designed short programmes and study attachments for experienced educationists.

Recent examples of tailor-made programmes include:
• 2-week course on primary trainer training (China)
• 10-week course on curriculum evaluation for Curriculum Capacity Project (Indonesia)
• 10-week course on teaching English at secondary level (Japan)
• 2-month attachment on Science & Technology Education (Japan)
• 1-week course on mentoring for TESOL (Romania)
• 2-year course on currriculum planning and active learning (Norway)

Fees: *determined on a course by course basis*

Enquiries and application forms: The Director, International Education; inter@education.leeds.ac.uk; T: 0113 343 4571

■ Junior Year Abroad

This scheme which allows undergraduates to spend up to a year studying at the University of Leeds.

Fees: 1 year: £6405; 1 semester: £3305

Applications: UCAS *(see Glossary)*

Enquiries: Study Abroad Office; jya@leeds.ac.uk; T: 0113 343 4046; F: 0113 343 3932

School of Education
21 University Road
LEICESTER LE1 7RF

T: 0116 252 3688
F: 0116 252 3653
E: cpdinfo@le.ac.uk
W: www.le.ac.uk

Dean of the Faculty of Education and Continuing Studies: Professor Ken Fogelman

CERTIFICATES / DIPLOMAS

■ PGCE Primary and Secondary

Length of course: 1 academic year f/t (38 weeks primary; 36 weeks secondary)
Entry requirements: UK honours degree or its equivalent or overseas degree or its equivalent from an approved university. Applicants must also have GCSE grade C or above in English Language, Maths (and Science for those born after 1 September 1979) or equivalents.
Course content: This is a course of initial teacher training, successful completion of which entitles students to teach in UK schools.
The Primary courses consist of:
• Early Years (age 3-8)
• Junior Years (age 7-11)
• An Educational Psychology tutorial group
• Students specialise in one of the following: English, Maths, Science, ICT, History, Geography
The Secondary course specialises in:
• English
• English with Media
• Modern Languages
• Social Science
• Biology
• Maths
• History
• Chemistry
• Geography
• Coordinated Science
• Physics
• Citizenship
Both courses have three major components:
• School experience
• Subject studies
• General professional studies
There are two periods of block attachment to schools.
Assessment: Course-work and satisfactory completion of practical teaching.
Enquiries: *PGCE Primary:* T: 0116 252 3677; *PGCE Secondary:* T: 0116 252 3689
Applications: via GTTR *(see Glossary)*
Fees: EU students: £1075
      Non-EU students: £7155

■ **Advanced Certificate in Educational Management**
Length of course: 30 hours
Entry requirements: Qualified teachers with appropriate experience.
Course content: There are two routes to the Advanced Certificate:
University-based: Successful completion of one module for the degree of MBA (Educational Management).
School-based: Presentation of a 5000-word assignment (an investigation of an education management topic relating to the school or college in which the candidate is currently working).
Successful completion of the school-based Certificate qualifies the candidate for exemption from one of the MBA (Education Management) modules.
Enquiries: EMDU, Queens Building, University Centre, Barrack Road, Northampton NN2 6AF; emdu@le.ac.uk; T: 01604 630180

■ **Advanced Certificate in TESOL**
This course is designed for practising teachers who require a higher qualification and further study in TESOL. It is offered as an independent module. In addition, it counts as one contributory module to our modular non-distance MA Professional Studies in Education programme (five modules and dissertation for a full programme) or to the MA Applied Linguistics/TESOL by distance learning.
The one-term modular course aims to give an overview of key areas in TESOL through the following units:
• Introduction to Key Issues
• History of English Language Teaching
• Listening
• Reading
• Vocabulary
• Learner Strategies & Learner Autonomy
• The Nature of Language Learning
• Looking at Language
• Speaking
• Writing
• Teaching Grammar
• Testing
Assessment: By structured tasks and a 4000-word assignment.
Fees: EU students: £750 per module
      Non-EU students: £850 per module
Enquiries: The Secretary, CPD - Distance Learning; T: 0116 252 3674

MASTER'S DEGREES

■ **MA in Applied Linguistics & TESOL**
Length of course: *Campus-based:*   1 year f/t; 2 years p/t
                  Distance Learning: 33 months
It is also possible to complete the degree through a combination of campus-based and distance learning study.
Entry requirements: First or second class UK degree, or Diploma in Education or its

overseas equivalent and two years' teaching experience. The course is suitable for experienced teachers, teacher trainers, materials and course designers, language planners and advisers or inspectors in TESOL in the UK or from overseas.

Course content: Students complete the following six modules:

- ELT Methodology (distance learners are awarded the Advanced Certificate in TESOL on successful completion of this module)
- Descriptions of Modern English
- Sociolinguistics & Discourse Analysis
- Second Language Acquisition
- Options
- Dissertation
  Options include:
  - Course & Syllabus Design
  - Testing & Evaluation
  - English for Specific Purposes
  - Management of ELT
  - Intercultural Communication
  - Young Learners & ELT
  - Teacher Education & ELT
  - Computer-Assisted Language Learning (campus-based only)
  - Materials Development & ELT (campus-based only)
  - Literature in ELT
  - Critical Discourse Analysis

Other options may be offered from time to time.

An II Skills Development Programme is offered to all campus-based participants.

Assessment: Course-work assignments and a 20,000 word dissertation.

Fees:

Campus-based:	EU students:	£2805 f/t; £1403 p/t
	Non-EU students: £7155	
Distance Learning (6 modules):	EU students:	£750 per module
	Non-EU students: £850 per module	

Enquiries: *Campus-based:* Ms Julie Thomson; T: 0116 252 3675
Distance Learning: Ms Helen Whitfield; T: 0116 252 5782

■ MA Professional Studies in Education

Length of course: 1 year f/t; up to 5 years p/t

Entry requirements: First or second class degree or Diploma in Education or its equivalent.

Course content: The course is organised on a modular basis. Students take a research methods module and select four advanced modules from a range which covers topics concerned with contemporary educational issues. The modules can be drawn from different areas but three modules should be in a related area of study. It is possible for students to gain exemption from one or possibly two advanced modules if they hold a Diploma in a relevant field.

Modules available in:

- School Improvement & Effectiveness
- Early Years Education

- Primary Education
- Educational Management
- Information & Communication Technology
- Educational Enquiry
- Special Education Needs
- Specific Learning Difficulties

Assessment: One assessed assignment for each module; dissertation.
Fees: EU students: £2805 f/t
        Non-EU students: £7155 f/t
Enquiries: The Secretary, CPD; T: 0116 252 3669; cpdinfo@le.ac.uk

■ MBA Educational Management
Length of course: 1 year f/t; up to 5 years p/t
Entry requirements: First or second class UK degree or its overseas equivalent
Course content: The course is organised on a modular basis. Students follow five specific modules in the area of education management:
- Leadership & Strategic Management
- Managing the Curriculum
- Human Resource Management
- Managing Finance & External Relations
- Research Methods

Assessment: An assessed assignment of 5000 words for each module; a 20,000-word dissertation.
Fees: £7155 f/t; £2250 p/t
Enquiries: EMDU, Queens Building, University Centre, Barrack Road, Northampton NN2 6AF; emdu@le.ac.uk; T: 01604 630180

■ MBA Educational Management (distance learning)
Length of course: Students may start the course at any time of the year and negotiate dates for the completion of assignments with their tutor. It is recommended that students spend no more than six months on each module.
Course content: The course is organised on the same modular basis as the MBA above (non-distance learning). It is possible for students to gain exemption in one or possibly two modules if they hold relevant post-graduate qualifications.
Assessment: An assessed 5000-word assignment for each of the five modules plus a 20,000-word dissertation.
Enquiries: EMDU, Queens Building, University Centre, Barrack Road, Northampton NN2 6AF; emdu@le.ac.uk; T: 01604 630180

■ MA Primary Education (distance learning)
Length of course: 1 year f/t; up to 5 years p/t
Entry requirements: First or second class degree or its equivalent Primary Teaching Qualification.The course is suitable for experienced teachers, school managers, teacher educators, advisers and inspectors.
The course is organised on a modular basis, the five modules being:
- Aspects of Child Development and Learning
- Aspects of Teaching

- Aspects of Primary Curriculum
- Issues in Primary Education
- Research Methods

Each module involves studying one unit and producing an assignment. It is possible for students to gain exemption in one or possibly two modules if they hold relevant post-graduate qualifications. Students may also take just one module to obtain an Advanced Certificate or four or five modules to obtain an Advanced Diploma or Post-graduate Diploma.

Assessment: A 5000-word assignment for each module; a 20,000-word dissertation.

Enquiries: T: 0116 252 3674

Fees: EU students: £750 per module
        Non-EU students: £850 per module

RESEARCH DEGREES

■ MSc, PhD

Length of course: *MSc:* 1 years f/t; 2 years p/t
        PhD: 4 years f/t; 6 years p/t

Entry requirements: First or upper second class honours degree and previous educational study of an advanced nature.

Course content: Supervision of individual research programmes is available in a variety of fields, including:

- Citizenship Studies, Human Rights Education & Social Inclusion
- Educational Leadership & Management
- Teaching & Learning
- TESOL & Applied Linguistics

Wherever possible, it is policy to associate individual researchers with one of the funded research programmes which are a feature of the School.

Assessment: Thesis

Fees: EU students: £2805pa f/t; £701pa p/t
        Non-EU students: £7155pa f/t; £3578 pa p/t

Enquiries: The Secretary, Research Degrees; aa90@le.ac.uk; T: 0116 252 3713; *or* The Postgraduate Tutor ; mm81@le.ac.uk; T: 0116 252 3682

■ EdD

Length of course: 2-3 years f/t; 3-5 years p/t

Entry requirements: Relevant higher degree; 3 years professional experience.

Course content: Modular structure of 20 units, of which five are represented by taught units and 15 by a 50,000-word thesis related to the main focus of study. Three streams:

- Educational Management & Administration
- Learning & Teaching
- Applied Linguistics & TESOL

and a compulsory research methods component.

Fees: EU students: £9000 (max)
        Non-EU students: £15,000 (max)

Enquiries: Professor Les Bell; lab19@le.ac.uk; T: 01604 630180

UNIVERSITY OF LINCOLN

International Institute for Educational Leadership
Brayford Pool
LINCOLN   LN6 7TS

T: 01522 886169
F: 01522 886023
E: iiel@lincoln.ac.uk
W: www.lincoln.ac.uk

Enquiries: Professor Angela Thody, Deputy Director, IIEL

The International Institute for Educational Leadership is a specialist post-graduate and research centre. One of our aims is to ensure that those who participate in our taught (professional) or research degree programmes are developing 'research in practice'. The assessed work you have to complete to attain your degree is intended to be put into practice to advance the needs of your organisations and your career development.

Our own research strengths, and areas in which we supervise research degrees, reflect this applied orientation. Our specialisms are in school business leadership, school academic leadership, learning and development and school re-engineering. We are consultants to the National College for School Leadership on bursarship programmes and on beginning principals' research. IIEL staff are members of European and international research teams. The IIEL was awarded full marks by the Quality Assurance Agency in 2001, one of only ten UK Education Departments to achieve this.

We offer post-graduate programmes for experienced professionals in senior posts, or those aspiring to senior management in schools, colleges or education government. These are available both part time (taught on 3-4 weekends during a year) or full time and there are some distance programmes also. The Institute's programmes focus on the work-related needs of our participants; all the assessed work required is the participant's individually chosen topics. Uniquely at EdD level, the assignments are also written for real 'audiences' of either refereed journals or for those within the participants' own organisations.

Internationalism is a central tenet of our approaches here and we welcome overseas as well as home and EU students. All our programmes have international Visiting Professors attached and each taught Unit includes speakers from abroad. IIEL staff travel widely disseminating their research at conferences abroad. On two of our programmes, study abroad is a requirement of the course and it is available for our other courses. Each year, the Institute organises at least one study trip abroad for participants on our programmes.

We provide personal support for participants in all our programmes. Everyone has a personal tutor throughout his/her programme. Tutorials are held during every taught Unit and you can also have telephone and email sessions in between Units. For dissertations and theses, two supervisors guide each student.

Participants requiring residence can chose from student accommodation or from a wide range of guest houses and hotels in Lincoln, which is a beautiful, mediaeval city in the East of England. The University has an International Advice and Development Worker for overseas' student support and an Accommodation Service. The University campus is all post-1996 with its modern buildings situated beside a marina. The

Glossary on page XI

campus includes health and sports facilities, a Chaplaincy and a well-equipped Learning Resources Centre. Shared workstations for post-graduates are available in the IIEL offices.

CERTIFICATES / DIPLOMAS

■ **Certificate in Education Learning & Development (distance learning)**
Length of course: 1 year (recommended, but can vary)
Entry requirements: Bachelor's degree or equivalent and teaching experience.
Course aims: Understanding and development of the theoretical and practical bases of learning and development, individual and organisational.
Course structure/content: The course consists of distance learning units with tutorial guidance. Students choose one of two programmes of study:
A. Units in
• Effective Self Development
• Psychology of Learning
• Individual Learning
• Organisational Learning
B.
• Research Skills
• A portfolio of a personal learning contract will be built up from other forthcoming courses or individual research.
• Those with units from other courses can apply for Accreditation of Prior Learning.
Assessment: For A: Assignments for three Units and Personal Learning Journal; For B: Research skills portfolio and learning contract assignments.
Fees: £595pa
Enquiries: Dr Marianne Hvizdak, Course Director; mhvizdak@lincoln.ac.uk

■ **Diploma in Education Learning & Development (distance learning)**
Length of course: 2 years (recommended, but can vary)
Entry requirements: Bachelor's degree or equivalent and teaching experience.
Course aims: Understanding and development of the theoretical and practical bases of learning and development, individual and organisational.
Course structure/content: See 'Course structure/content' under *Certificate in Education Learning & Development* above. To earn the Diploma, students undertake both progammes A and B.
Assessment: Assignments for three Units; Personal Learning Journal; Research Skills Portfolio; learning contract assignments.
Fees: £595pa
Enquiries: Dr Marianne Hvizdak, Course Director; mhvizdak@lincoln.ac.uk

■ **Diploma in Educational Leadership (International)**
Length of course: 1.5 years
Entry requirements: Bachelor's degree or equivalent; experience in leading learning in educational settings.
Course aims: Developing leaders to improve learning at all levels of an organisation; investigating leadership in relation to organisational and individual practice; understanding the international environment for educational organisations.

Glossary on page XI   117

Course structure/content: The course consists of five 3-day units in Year I and three 3-day units in Year II. Units studied:
- Leadership and Learning
- Quality and Effectiveness
- Organisations & Change
- High Performance & Teams
- Strategic Planning
- Resource Management
- Managing Student Achievement
- Research Skills

Each students also undertakes an international experience.

Assessment: Personal learning journal; research plans; assignments for each unit.

Fees: EU students: £2000 p/t
        Non-EU students: £4000 p/t
        Fees payable in instalments.

Enquiries: Trevor Male, Director of Headteacher Development; tmale@lincoln.ac.uk

MASTER'S DEGREES

■ MSc Education Learning & Development (distance learning)

Length of course: 3 years (recommended, but can vary)

Entry requirements: Bachelor's degree or equivalent and teaching experience.

Course aims: Understanding and development of the theoretical and practical bases of learning and development, individual and organisational.

Course structure/content: See 'Course structure/content' under *Certificate in Education Learning & Development* above. To earn the MSc, students undertake both progammes A and B plus research study with dissertation or portfolio.

Assessment: Assignments for three units; personal learning journal; research skills portfolio; learning contract assignments; 20,000-word dissertation.

Fees: £595pa

Enquiries: Dr Marianne Hvizdak, Course Director; mhvizdak@lincoln.ac.uk

■ MBA in Education for Bursars of Self-managing Schools

This programme is available in Lincoln or at the University of Melbourne, Australia. Enquiries for Melbourne should be sent to Lincoln.

Length of course: 2-3 years p/t

Entry requirements: Experience in school business management and Bachelors degree or equivalent (ca 25% of our entrants have a first degree, but the majority have a variety of equivalents such as Advanced Diplomas in Management or Secretaryship, NVQs, various types of accountancy, legal or teaching qualifications.

Course aims: Developing participants' leadership and management skills; introducing international perspectives; advanced study into the theoretical bases of educational leadership and management.

Course structure/content: Six 3-day residential units in Year I, plus individually supervised evidence-based enquiry. Units taught:
- Leadership & Management
- Competency Development

- Quality & Effectiveness
- Managing Change
- Leading and Managing Staff
- Futures Thinking & Strategic Planning
- Financial Resource Management
- Managing External Relations
- Research Skills
- Action Project Management Study
- International Experience (optional)

Assessment: Personal learning journal; research plans; four school-based assignments; 20,000-word action project management study.

Fees: EU students: £3000 p/t
      Non-EU students: 54000 p/t
      Fees payable in instalments.

Enquiries: Elizabeth Wood, Director of Bursarship Development; ewood@lincoln.ac.uk

■ MBA in Educational Leadership (International)

Length of course: 2-3 years p/t

Entry requirements: Bachelors degree or equivalent; experience in leading learning in educational settings.

Course aims: Developing leaders to improve learning at all levels of an organisation; investigating leadership in relation to organisational and individual practice; understanding the international environment for educational organisations.

Course structure/content: Six 3-day residential units, plus individually supervised evidence-based enquiry. Units taught:

- Leadership & Learning
- Quality & Effectiveness
- Organisations & Change
- High Performance & Teams
- Strategic Planning
- Resource Management
- Managing Student Achievement
- Research Skills
- International experience
- Evidence-based enquiry for Action Project Management Study

Each students also undertakes an international experience.

Assessment: Personal learning journal; research plans; four school-based assignments; 20,000-word evidence-based enquiry.

Fees: EU students: £3000 p/t
      Non-EU students: £5000 p/t
      Fees payable in instalments.

Enquiries: Trevor Male, Director of Headteacher Development; tmale@lincoln.ac.uk

RESEARCH DEGREES

■ **EdD in International Educational Leadership**

Length of course: 3-6 years p/t

Entry requirements: Master's degree in management or education management or equivalent; experience in educational leadership.

Course aims: To provide participants with work-related academic development, to advance their abilities to undertake advanced research and its dissemination and to gain confidence in applying theories to practice.

Course structure/content: Four taught units per year over the first two and a half years; dissertation tutorials individually to completion. Units taught:
• Contemporary International Issues
• Leadership
• Organisational Structures
• Quality & Effectiveness
• Research Methods

Each student undertakes individual international study.

Note: Plans are being discussed for summer schools for this programme, likely to commence in 2003.

Assessment: 4000-word assignments for each unit; 30-40,000-word dissertation; oral defence for dissertation preparation and final viva.

Fees: EU students: £5980 p/t
      Non-EU students: £13,000 p/t (f/t fees on application)
      Fees payable in instalments.

Enquiries: Professor Angela Thody, Director Doctoral Programmes; athody@lincoln.ac.uk

■ **EdD in International Educational Leadership**

This programme is suitable for those who are practitioners in educational organisations and those who wish to develop careers in higher education lecturing.

Length of course: 2-3 years f/t; 3-5 years p/t

Entry requirements: Applicants with Bachelor degrees enter for MPhil and usually convert to the PhD route after one year if their abilities and area of study are suitable; Master's degree needed for PhD direct entry.

Course aims: To develop candidates able to critically investigate and evaluate a research topic, to contribute to knowledge, to understand research methods, to present and defend a thesis.

Course structure/content: Research methods units in
• Philosophy of Research
• Qualitative & Quantitative Methods

Individual tutorials with supervisors for thesis preparation.

Research areas:
• School & College Academic Leadership
• School Business Leadership
• Followership
• School Re-engineering
• Learning & Development

Assessment: *MPhil:* 4000-word thesis; *PhD:* 80,000-word thesis and viva.
Fees: EU students: £940pa p/t; £2200 f/t
      Non-EU students: £2280pa p/t; £5589 f/t
Enquiries: Professor Angela Thody, Director Doctoral Programmes; athody@lincoln.ac.uk

OTHER COURSES

■ Doctoral Associateship
Three to four programmes are offered each year.
Length of course: 3 days per programme
Entry requirements: This is a non-accredited course with open entry; however, a master's degree in management or education management is advised.
Course aims: To keep participants up-to-date with cutting-edge thinking internationally.
Course content: 2002/03 courses:
• Quality & Organisational Effectiveness (17-19 March 2003 or 27-29 March 2003)
• Leadership (15-17 May 2003)
Assessment: None. Attendance certificates are provided, registering the participant as a Lincoln Doctoral Associate.
Fees: £250 per course
Enquiries: Professor Angela Thody, Director Doctoral Programmes; athody@lincoln.ac.uk

Department of Education
19 Abercromby Square
LIVERPOOL L69 7ZG

W: www.liv.ac.uk/education

Head of Department: Dr Anne Qualter
Enquiries: Ingrid Harper; ingridh@liverpool.ac.uk; T: 0151 794 2513; F: 0151 794 2512

MASTER'S DEGREES

■ MEd

Length of course: 1 year *(admission in October)*

Entry requirements: Eligibility is related to previous educational achievement and/or professional experience. Credit may be given for relevant qualifications previously acquired at other institutions or in some cases for relevant professional experience. Applicants who do not have English as a first language must possess a suitable English Language qualification or provide other evidence that they satisfy this requirement.

Course content: The programme addresses a range of issues relating to educational ideas and practices, examining these from both a personal and a social perspective. It is designed for students from a wide variety of backgrounds who have an interest in educational theory and practice and is particularly suitable for those who are not at present working in the school sector in the UK.

Fees: EU students: £1260 (f/t)
Non-EU students: £8532 (f/t)

School of Education, Community & Social Sciences
IM Marsh Campus, Barkhill Road
LIVERPOOL L17 6BD

T: 0151 231 5240/5201
F: 0151 231 5399
W: www.livjm.ac.uk/ecs

Director of School: Professor Vince Gardiner
Head of Education: Dr Tricia Meers
Head of PE, Sport & Dance: Professor Pat Shenton
Enquiries: p.j.dolan@livjm.ac.uk

BACHELOR DEGREES

■ BA Hons Primary with QTS

Length of course: 4 years
Course content: Students study English, Maths and Science and how to teach these subjects to the 5-11 age range. A specialist subject is chosen from one of the three. Courses in PE and Art & Design Education are also included in the programme.

■ BA Hons Secondary Physical Education with QTS

Length of course: 4 years
Course content: Students follow theoretical and practical study in PE through sustained periods in schools.

■ BA Hons Primary and Secondary (KS 2/3) with QTS

Length of course: 3 years
Course content: The course prepares students to teach across the upper primary and lower secondary school range. A specialist subject is chosen from one of the following: PE, Design & Technology, Science Education or Maths Education. A knowledge and understanding of the core curriculum (English, Maths, Science) is also developed.

■ BA Hons Childhood Studies

Length of course: 3 years
Course content: The course provides an opportunity to study children and issues related to childhood. Issues include:
• Education
• Health
• Law & Social Policy
• Sociology of Childhood

■ BA Hons Education & Learning

This course is under development to start in January 2003.
Length of course: 3-5 years
Course aims/content: The course is designed to meet the needs of those who wish to study part-time and those working in a para-professional role in schools. It will suit a range of career aspirations linked to education and will serve as a route to take a postgraduate qualified teacher course.

■ **BEd Secondary with QTS / 2-year PGCE Information Technology**
Length of course: 2 years
Course content: A shortened route for applicants over the age of 21 and with appropriate prior study and experience in IT. Can be followed as PGCE for graduates in other disciplines.
Fees: EU students: £1075
Non-EU students: £7600

CERTIFICATES / DIPLOMAS / MASTER'S DEGREES

■ **PGCE**
Length of course: 1 year (36 weeks) f/t
Entry requirements: A degree in an appropriate subject.
Course content: Specialist subject modules relate to teaching in schools and provide opportunities for students to relate knowledge from their degree studies to the school curriculum. Students spend two-thirds of their time in schools. Specialist subjects:
• Art & Design
• D&T
• Early Years
• MFL
• PE
• Science
Fees: EU students: £1075
Non-EU students: £7600
We also offer a flexible PGCE route which involves a needs analysis and a tailored training programme of variable length depending on previous experience. This could be suitable for overseas trained teachers wishing to obtain QTS to teach in English schools. Specialist Subjects: Art, D&T, MFL, PE, Science.
NOTE: PGCE students from the EU may be eligible for a training salary of £6000 per annum.

■ **PGCert in Teaching & Learning in Higher Education**
This is a part-time inservice 180-credit programme for HE teachers accredited by SEDA.
Course content: A wide-ranging introduction to the skills and knowledge needed to be an effective HE teacher.
Fees: EU students: £15.60 per credit
Non-EU students: £42.50 per credit

■ **PGDip/MA in Teaching & Learning in Higher Education**
A progression from the Certificate programme *(above)*, this is a professional development route for HE Lecturers. The Certificate, Diploma and MA programmes are work-based and participants submit a portfolio of assessment tasks related to their own professional practice.

■ **PGCert / PGDip / MA Education**

<u>Course content:</u> This part-time programme offers a number of routes which enable students to specialise in one of the following:

- D&T
- Education Management & Subject Leadership
- ICT
- PE
- PSHE & Citizenship
- School Improvement
- Science Education
- SEN
- Teaching & Learning

Other areas available on enquiry.

Suitable candidates can be accredited for prior learning and experience or take a Learning at Work (LaWP) route.

<u>Fees:</u> EU students: £15.60 per credit
          Non-EU students: £42.50 per credit

■ **MA Artist Teachers**

This artist-teachers scheme is an innovative professional development project that aims to assist artist-teachers to review and develop their own creative practice.

<u>Fees:</u> EU students: £15.60 per credit
          Non-EU students: £42.50 per credit

<u>RESEARCH DEGREES</u>

The School supports a range of research students following projects linked to research expertise.

UNIVERSITY OF LONDON, GOLDSMITHS

Educational Studies Department   T: 020 7919 7300
Goldsmiths College   F: 020 7919 7313
New Cross   W: www.gold.ac.uk
LONDON   SE14 6NW

Enquiries / Admission: *UK/EU students:* admissions@gold.ac.uk
     Non-EU students: international-office@gold.ac.uk

Founded in 1891, Goldsmiths is one of the liveliest colleges of the University of London. It is situated in New Cross, South East London, a vibrant urban area with excellent public transport connections to and from Central London. It is also ideal for getting to the Continent - within easy travelling distance of the Kent ports of Folkestone and Dover, and close to Waterloo International Station by train.
Goldsmiths has a welcoming atmosphere and caters to students' needs with a wide range of facilities. It attracts students from a diversity of social and cultural backgrounds from across the EU and an increasing number from overseas.
Goldsmiths specialises in the study of creative, cultural and social processes; it has a long well-established reputation for teacher education, and is strongly committed to widening participation and life-long learning. The Educational Studies Department encompasses a wide range of teaching and research interests and expertise. It has professorial chairs in Education, Educational Policy & Management and Language & Culture in Education. Research projects have included Technology Education, Modes of Teacher Education, Personal & Social Development in Schools, Early Childhood Education, Health Education, Education for Sustainability and The Future of Comprehensive Education in General and the 14-19 Curriculum in Particular. The Department has recently hosted two ESRC research projects in Bilingualism & Biculturalism in Education and Educational Identities & the Consumption of Tradition. It is currently engaged in a Leverhulme Research Project on Children's Home & School Literacy Practices in collaboration with King's College and Brighton University.
The Department provides a comprehensive programme of courses including undergraduate BA Hons with QTS, Postgraduate Certificate in Education (PGCE), postgraduate research, taught Master's degrees, Master's in research, as well as employment-based routes into teaching. Full- and part-time courses are available in most areas. These provide opportunities for teachers and others working in education to undertake further study and professional development.

BACHELOR DEGREES

■ BA Hons in Education (Primary) with QTS
Length of course: 3 years f/t
Entry requirements: 2 A-levels or equivalent and grade A-C GCE O-level or GCSE in English, Science and Maths or equivalent qualifications; applications from mature students are considered on merit. Selection is by interview.
Course content: The course provides a balance between a general introduction to the range of subjects taught in Primary schools and development of students in a subject strength. Students specialise in two subjects in year three. The course includes a substantial amount of school-based work in which students are supported by College

tutors and school teachers in partnership. This element of the course enables students to develop their theoretical and professional understanding and expertise.

Fees: EU students: £1100
      Non-EU students: £7845

■ BAEd Hons Design & Technology (Secondary)

Length of course: 4 years f/t

Entry requirements: Normally 2 A-levels or equivalent in a design-related area; GCSEs in English and Maths; applications from mature students welcomed. Selection is by interview.

Course content: The course consists of two main strands:

- Design Practice, covering
  - Design
  - Teaching & Learning through Design & Technology
  - Communication
  - Technology
  - History of Product Design
  - Manufacturing in wide range of resistant and compliant materials
- Professional Practice, covering
  - History, Philosophy & Psychology of Education
  - Management of the Design & Technology Curriculum

The course includes a substantial amount of school-based work in partner schools in which students are supported by both college and school-based tutors.

Enquiries: Juliet Sprake; j.sprake@gold.ac.uk; T: 020 7919 7785

Fees: EU students: £1100
      Non-EU students: £7845

CERTIFICATES / DIPLOMAS

■ PGCE Primary and Secondary

Length of course: 1 academic year f/t (Primary: 38 weeks; Secondary: 36 weeks)

Entry requirements: UK degree or its equivalent, or overseas degree or its equivalent from an approved university; English and Maths certificates.

Course content: Two courses are available:

- A primary course offering two age specialisms: Early Years (3-8) and Junior Years (7-11).
- A secondary course with specialisms in: Art & Design, Biology, Chemistry, D&T, Drama, English, Geography, General Science, Maths, Modern Languages (French, German, Spanish), Music, Physics, Social Science with Citizenship

The courses have three major components:

- School experience (organised in blocks spread over the three terms)
- Educational and professional studies
- The application of subjects to the learning of children and young people

Assessment: Assessed course work and satisfactory completion of school-based work.

Applications: via GTTR (see Glossary)

Fees: EU students: nil
      Non-EU students: £8140

MASTER'S DEGREES

■ MA in Education: Culture, Language & Identity

This is a new MA programme which adopts a broad-based approach to studying the effects of social and cultural issues in different fields of educational practice and theory. The diversity of everyday social contexts means that educators need to develop a cultural sensitivity to respond effectively to differences in identity and culture. The programme is aimed at teachers, social workers, gallery, museum and library educators, as well as anyone interested in educational practice and theory who wishes to investigate cultural processes and their effect on education. The course aims to:

- enhance the student's understanding and critical awareness of educational theory and practice drawing upon issues of culture, language and identity
- develop inclusive and alternative perspectives and strategies to teaching and learning through a process of critical reflection
- help students to apply their developing understanding to educational practices and issues in their institutions and elsewhere
- prepare students to take up posts of responsibility in schools, colleges and other educational settings

Length of course: 1 year f/t; normally 2 years p/t (or an approved combination of both)

Entry requirements: Normally an honours degree (2:2 or above) in a relevant subject, together with appropriate educational experience/qualification. Non-graduates and others may be eligible for entry via a qualifier's route, with College advice and guidance.

Course structure: This is a modular degree offering the opportunity to explore various areas of education to develop a more inclusive and inter-cultural approach to teaching and learning. Courses will cover the following topics:

- Culture, Language & Identity in Education
- Diaspora, Race & Culture and Education
- Bilingualism & Biculturalism in Education
- Visual Culture & Education
- Design, Innovation & the Curriculum
- Early Childhood Education for a Diverse Society
- Children's Literature & Cultural Diversity
- Multilingualism & Early Literacy Learning
- Masculinities, Femininities & Identities Education
- The Language & Politics of Disability
- Researching Culture, Language & Identity in Education
- Culture, Pedagogy & Curriculum

The MA consists of three elements:

- *Compulsory core taught module:*
  Culture, Language and Identity in Education (1 credit)
- *Taught option modules:*
  Students take option modules to a total of either 3 or 4 credits, depending on whether a dissertation or a report is chosen.
- *Compulsory core research module:*
  Either dissertation (2 credits) or a report (1 credit)

To obtain the MA, students need to achieve six MA Education credits, ie 180 credit accumulation and transfer (CAT) points at Masters ('M') level.

Assessment: Single credit modules are assessed by assignments of 5000 words; dissertation (2 credits) is 20,000 words; report (1 credit) is 10,000 words.

Enquiries: Joan Lofters; j.lofters@gold.ac.uk; T: 044 207 919 7302

Fees: EU students: £2870 f/t; £355 per module p/t

Non-EU students: £7845

RESEARCH DEGREES

■ MPhil, PhD

Length of course: *MPhil:* 2-3 years f/t; 3-4 years p/t

PhD: 3-4 years f/t; 4-6 years p/t

Registration can be changed from p/t to f/t and vice-versa.

Entry requirements: UK degree or its equivalent, or overseas degree or its equivalent from an approved university at 2:2 class or above in a relevant subject together with educational experience and/or qualification (a degree in a non-related field may be considered). In some instances candidates may be required to sit a qualifying examination.

Course content: The course will develop the students capacity to:
• identify appropriate issues of educational significance for enquiry
• select appropriate methods and methodologies by which to investigate these
• appreciate the epistemological and technical assumptions that underpin this choice
• design and execute well-founded enquiries
• analyse and interpret findings with accuracy, rigour and originality
• identify the practical and professional implications of educational enquiry

Students will be offered an induction and research training programme at the start of the course and will be assigned a supervisor with whom there will be regular tutorial contact. The student's progress will be appraised each year.

Initially students register for a MPhil. When an agreed part of the research and training programme has satisfactorily been completed, application can be made to upgrade registration to a PhD. For full-time students this usually occurs after 18 months, for part-time students after two to three years.

Research areas: The Department has Academic/Research Groupings in the following broad areas:
• Language & Culture in Education
• Promoting Equity & Social Justice
• Analysing Curriculum Policy in Practice

We can offer support in:
• Art in Education
• Bilingualism in Education
• Classroom Enquiry
• Comprehensive Education
• Curriculum Studies
• Design & Technology Education

- Equal Opportunities in Education
- Issues in Sexuality & Identity and Gender Studies
- Home/School Relationship
- Power, Knowledge & Schooling
- Space, Time & Education
- *Other fields by negotiation*

Assessment: Thesis - 60,000 (max) words for MPhil; 80,000 (max) for PhD; examination by thesis and viva voce.

Enquiries: Joan Lofters; j.lofters@gold.ac.uk; T: 020 7919 7302; F: 020 7919 7313

Fees: EU students: £2870
      Non-EU students: £7845

Institute of Education	T: 020 7612 6000
20 Bedford Way	F: 020 7612 6126
LONDON	E: info@ioe.ac.uk
WC1H 0AL	W: www.ioe.ac.uk

Director of the Institute: Professor Geoff Whitty

The Institute of Education, a graduate college of the University of London, celebrates its 100th anniversary in 2002. The Institute offers a wide range of initial teacher training courses and courses leading to higher degrees and advanced diplomas in all areas of education and related aspects of the social sciences.

Long recognised as a world centre of educational enquiry, the Institute has obtained high rankings in each of the four research assessment exercises conducted by the UK university funding bodies. The scale and excellence of the Institute's research attract large numbers of students from all over the world keen to work with scholars at the forefront of education. In the 2000/01 academic year over 400 international students participated in Institute courses.

The Institute is located in central London, close to other colleges of the University of London, the University of London Union, shops, theatres, cinemas, galleries, museums, restaurants, bars and cafes. Its hall of residence and self-catering student accommodation are nearby. Located within the main Institute building is the Newsam Library, the largest university-based collection in Europe of learned books and periodicals concerned with educational studies.

Pre-sessional and in-sessional language courses help students with the English appropriate to their studies, help them cope with cultural differences and give opportunities for practice. A number of student societies provide international students with a welcome break from their studies, including the African, Japanese, Latin American and Multicultural societies. The annual Multicultural Extravaganza features dance, music, poetry and drama from many countries.

BACHELOR DEGREES

- **BEd for Serving Teachers**

Enquiries: ITE Section, Registry; bed.enquiries@ioe.ac.uk; T: 020 7612 6108; F: 020 7612 6041

CERTIFICATES / DIPLOMAS

- **PGCE Primary / Secondary / Post-Compulsory**
- **Further Education Teacher's Certificate**

Enquiries: ITE Section, Registry; pgce.enquiries@ ioe.ac.uk; T: 020 7612 6123; F: 020 7612 6041

- **Advanced Diploma in Psychology**
- **Certificate in Primary Health Care Education & Development**
- **Certificated Course in Online Education & Training**

Enquiries: Further Professional Development Section, Registry; fpd.enquiries@ioe.ac.uk; T: 020 7612 6101; F: 020 7612 6097

MASTER'S DEGREES

- **MA/MSc**

In over 40 subjects, including curriculum subjects and all levels of education from early years to post-compulsory, plus Management, Educational Psychology and the foundation disciplines of education.

- **Master of Teaching**
- **Higher Education Management**

Enquiries: Further Professional Development Section, Registry; fpd.enquiries@ioe.ac.uk; T: 020 7612 6101; F: 020 7612 6097

RESEARCH DEGREES

- **MPhil, PhD**
- **MRes (Educational and Social Research)**
- **EdD**
- **DEdPsy**

Enquiries: Research Degrees Section, Registry; doc.enquiries@ioe.ac.uk; T: 020 7612 6122; F: 020 7612 6097

OTHER COURSES

- **Short Courses**
- **Professional Development Courses**

Enquiries: The Registry; fpd.enquiries@ioe.ac.uk or (for Associateships) doc.enquiries@ioe.ac.uk; T: 020 7612 6100/6103; F: 020 7612 6097

- **INSET**

Enquiries: Dean Huit, CPD/INSET Department; d.huit@ioe.ac.uk; T: 020 7612 6591; F: 020 7612 6600

Department of Education & Professional Studies
Franklin Wilkins Building
Waterloo Road
LONDON SE1 9NN

T: 020 7848 2929
F: 020 7848 3182
E: programme.enquiries@kcl.ac.uk
W: www.kcl.ac.uk/education

Head of Department: Professor Deryn Watson

King's College, London, founded in 1829, has been involved in the field of Education since 1890. Today the Department of Education & Professional Studies continues that involvement through teaching and training, research, curriculum development and international collaboration. The Department has achieved high ratings in all four national Research Assessment Exercises. It is one of the largest university departments of education in the UK and is situated in central London, in the heart of London's South Bank Complex with the main King's College campus facing it across the Thames. The Department has an extensive range of facilities including three Science and two Maths education laboratories, an educational computing suite and a library. Being part of the University of London, King's College students have access to other library facilities throughout London.

CERTIFICATES / DIPLOMAS

■ PGCE
Length of course: 1 year
Entry requirements: A degree closely related to the subject you intend to teach in; passes in English Language and Maths at GCE O-level or GCSE grade C or an equivalent qualification. For Modern Languages you must be able to offer two languages, one of which should be French; for ICT you must have experience of some applications of ICT.
Course content: A combination of College-based work and two school placements plus teaching on educational issues for all subjects. Subjects offered:
• Classics
• English
• ICT
• Maths
• MFL (French, German and Spanish)
• RE
• Science (Biology, Physics or Chemistry)
Assessment: Coursework; assessed teaching practice.

■ PGDip in Health Education & Health Promotion
Length of course: 1 year f/t; 2-4 years p/t
Entry requirements: Good first degree and relevant experience
Course content: 6 modules
Assessment: Coursework
Fees: EU students: £2805 f/t; £390 per 20 credits p/t
        Non-EU students: £8800 f/t; £1467 per 20 credits p/t

Glossary on page XI

MASTER'S DEGREES

- **MA in Applied Language Studies in Education**
- **MA in Classics Education**
- **MA in Computers in Education**
- **MA in Education & Professional Studies**
- **MA in English in Education**
- **MA in Education Management**
- **MA in Language, Ethnicity & Education**
- **MA in Maths Education**
- **MA in MFL Education**
- **MA in Science Education**
- **MA in Urban Education**

Length of course: 1 year f/t; 2-4 years p/t

Entry requirements: Degree (2.2 or above); appropriate professional experience in education.

Course content: The MA degrees are suitable for teachers, education advisers and other education professionals. The degree, although firmly based on practical experience, places an emphasis on the theoretical study of the subject and programmes can be tailored to focus on the work conducted in your own institution. The programmes of study will provide you with a sound basis for future research in education. Each degree has a specialist subject focus of at least 50% of the degree. The degrees are modular and will be tailored to suit your individual professional and academic interests. There are currently 56 modules available, which are offered in alternate years.

Fees: EU students: £2805 f/t; £390 per 20 credits p/t
Non-EU students: £8800 f/t; £1467 per 20 credits p/t

- **MA in ELT & Applied Linguistics**

Length of course: 1 year f/t; 2 years p/t

Entry requirements: Good relevant degree and three years' full-time TESOL experience; 6 IELTS score.

Course content: Two compulsory courses, two optional courses; dissertation.

Assessment: Dissertation and coursework.

Fees: *EU students:* £2805 f/t; £1405 p/t; *Non-EU students:* £8800 f/t; £4400 p/t

Enquiries: MA ELT/Applied Linguistics Administrator; T: 020 7848 3725

- **MSc in Health Education & Health Promotion**

Length of course: 1 year f/t; 2-4 years p/t

Entry requirements: Good first degree and relevant experience.

Course content: 7 modules

Assessment: Dissertation and coursework.

Fees: EU students: £2805 f/t; £390 per 20 credits p/t
Non-EU students: £8800 f/t; £1467 per 20 credits p/t

- **MA in Religious Education**

Length of course: 1 year f/t; 2-4 years p/t

Entry requirements: Good first degree and relevant experience.

Course content: 6 modules (4 compulsory, 2 options)

Assessment: Dissertation and coursework.
Fees: EU students: £2805 f/t; £390 per 20 credits p/t
    Non-EU students: £8800 f/t; £1467 per 20 credits p/t

■ **MA in Youth Ministry & Theological Education**
Length of course: 1 year f/t; 2-4 years p/t
Course content: Four compulsory modules and two options.
Assessment: Dissertation and coursework.
Fees: EU students: £2805 f/t; £390 per 20 credits p/t
    Non-EU students: £8800 f/t; £1467 per 20 credits p/t

RESEARCH DEGREES

■ **MPhil, PhD**
Entry requirements: Second class honours degree; a teaching qualification or equivalent; two or more years of research in education *or* a Masters Degree of the University of London *or* a professional or other qualification obtained by written examination and approved by the School of Education.
Research areas: Areas of particular interest include:
• Mathematics Education
• Science Education
• Centre for Public Policy Research
• Centre for Theology, Religion & Culture
• Language in Education
• Centre for the Advancement of Thinking
• Assessment
• Professional Change & Professional Development
Assessment: Upgrade report from MPhil to PhD, Thesis, Viva Voce
Fees: *EU students:* £2805 f/t; £1560 p/t; *Non-EU students:* £8650 f/t; £4325 p/t
Enquiries and applications: Ms Chiz Dube; T: 020 7848 3089

■ **EdD** (taught doctorate)
Length of course: 4 years (min) p/t
Entry requirements: Master's degree in Education or a related discipline.
Course content: Six taught modules, depending on chosen specialism, but including a double module on Methods of Inquiry and a module on the Foundations of Professionalism; individually supervised Institution Focused Study; individually supervised Research Thesis (min. 25,000 words).
Specialisms:
• Maths Education
• Science Education
• IT (Computer) Education
• Language & Education
• Educational Assessment
• Religion & Culture
Fees: *EU students:* £1560; *Non-EU students:* £4325

Faculty of Education
Oxford Road
MANCHESTER M13 9PL

T: 0161 275 3463
F: 0161 275 3528
E: janet.grimshaw@man.ac.uk
W: www.man.ac.uk/education

The Faculty of Education is one of the oldest in Britain. It was founded in 1890 and has been at the forefront of many major advances, pioneered by educational research. Its work is now organised around five Research and Teaching Groups:
• Educational Support & Inclusion
• Human Communication & Deafness
• Language & Literacy Studies in Education
• Learning, Teaching & Assessment
• Management & Institutional Development
The groups offer a choice of over 30 courses ranging from Certificate, Diploma, Bachelor and Master's degrees through to Doctoral studies. The MEd degree is available by modular study and offers a choice of some 80 modules. Courses of special interest to those from overseas include:
• Communications, Education and Technology
• Educational Leadership and School Improvement
• Educational Psychology
• Further Professional Studies in Hearing Impairment
• Special & Inclusive Education
• TESOL
Of a full-time student body of 900, over 200 are from outside the UK representing some 60 plus countries; the majority are postgraduates employed in senior posts at home who bring with them a wealth of experience and knowledge and make an important academic contribution to our work. All courses are open to UK and overseas students. Facilities include the John Rylands University Library which has over three million volumes, a specialist department library and a primary education resource centre. Technical facilities include a computer support unit and five computer laboratories. All computers are connected to the Internet and have email. There is also a television studio and photographic/science/technology laboratories.

BACHELOR DEGREES

■ BSc Hons Audiology
Length of course: 4 years f/t
Course aims/content: This new course aims to provide a broad understanding of audiological principles, theory and knowledge. Appropriate learning opportunities for students to gain a comprehensive knowledge that can be translated into thoughtful, reflective and quality practice will be provided. In addition, the programme aims to offer, monitor and evaluate a wide range of appropriate clinical experience within audiology. Students are also equipped with a range of transferable skills that will promote a commitment to professional development and lifelong learning.
Fees: EU students: £1100
       Non-EU students: £9950

■ **BA Hons Language, Literacy & Communication**
Length of course: 3 years f/t
Entry requirements: A-levels (BBC) or equivalent; IELTS score 7 for students whose first language is not English.
Course content: The core elements of the degree - language, literacy, communication - are related to some of the Faculty's key areas of scholarship and research. The course is of particular interest to those who are considering a career in primary school teaching and offers broad experience of the disciplines that underlie education as an academic area, as well as valuable transferable skills for a range of other careers.
Fees: EU students: £1100
      Non-EU students: £7650

■ **BA Hons Learning Disability Studies**
Length of course: 3 years f/t; 6 years p/t
Course aims/content: This new course aims to encourage critical thought about disability, difference and current developments in the fields of learning disability, examining how and why services for people with learning difficulties have developed as they have. The programme aims to prepare people for a variety of work roles in areas of social care and/or education.
Fees: EU students: £1100
      Non-EU students: £7650

■ **BA Hons Leisure Management**
Length of course: 3 years
Course content: The course combines academic study with professional training. It covers historical, psychological, sociological and economic approaches to leisure together with management skills including marketing and accounting. A work placement scheme in the leisure industry is incorporated.
Fees: EU students: £1100
      Non-EU students: £7650

■ **BSc Hons Speech & Language Therapy**
Length of course: 4 years
Course content: The course comprises academic and practical work in subjects relevant to the practice of Speech Therapy and is taught in the Faculties of Education, Arts, Science & Engineering and Medicine. Clinical experience is acquired throughout the course in both departmental and external clinics.
Fees: EU students: £1100
      Non-EU students: £9950

DIPLOMAS

■ **Postgraduate Diploma in Profound Learning Disability & Multi-Sensory Impairment**
Length of course: 2 years by distance mode
Entry requirements: QTS or equivalent professional qualifications.
Course content: Students complete six course units, undertake a supervised practical placement and produce a professional portfolio of observations.

■ Diploma in Advanced Study in Education
Length of course: 9 months f/t; 2 years p/t
Entry requirements: Open to both graduates and suitably qualified non-graduates.
Course content: The course is designed for experienced teachers in schools and Further Education wishing to obtain an advanced qualification or for non-graduates wishing to undertake the taught degree of MEd. The latter will be assessed on two course units available both for the Diploma and Master programmes. On successful completion of two course units at Masters level they would transfer to the MEd for the remainder of the course. Course units for the Diploma are the same as those for the degree of Master.

■ Diploma in Advanced Study in Communications, Education & Technology
This course is designed for educators from the UK and overseas with an interest in the use of mass media for educational purposes and provides an introduction to the study of mass media systems and to the use of audio-visual media for teaching and learning.
Length of course: 12 months f/t; 2 years p/t
Entry requirements: Open to both graduates and suitably qualified non-graduates
Course content: Contributors to the course include broadcasters, journalists and other media professionals. Practical project work and visits to media organisations can be arranged to meet individual needs. Attention is given to the development of interpersonal communication skills through experiential groupwork.

■ Diploma in Advanced Study in Educational Leadership & School Improvement
This course is for experienced teachers in colleges or primary and secondary schools who already have some area of responsibility or are aspiring to such a position.
Length of course: 1 year f/t; 2 years p/t
Entry requirements: Open to both graduates and certain other suitably qualified and experienced non-graduates.
Course content: The course has the following components: Leadership & Management of Schools as Organisations; Practitioner-based Enquiry; School Improvement; School Effectiveness; Management of Development & Change in Education; Leadership & Management of People in Schools.

■ PGCE Primary and Secondary
Length of course: 9 months f/t
Entry requirements: Graduate or equivalent.
Course content: There is a large primary group and the following main subjects are available in the secondary level group: D&T, Economics & Business Studies, English, IT, Maths, MFL, Science.
Fees: £9950

MASTER'S DEGREES

■ MSc in Audiology
This degree is suitable for those wishing to train as audiological scientists (NHS or private hearing health care) and is accredited for this purpose by the British Association of Audiological Scientists. It is also suitable for doctors in community paediatrics

who wish to specialise in audiology, for audiological physicians in training grades and for teachers of the deaf wishing to extend their knowledge-base and experience in order to develop their role as educational audiologists.

Length of course: 12 months f/t; 2 years p/t

Course content: Theoretical modules include:

- Auditory Science
- Basic Audiological Assessment
- Paediatric Audiology & Communication
- Research Methods
- Sensory Aids
- Adult Hearing Loss
- Disabilities Associated with Adult Hearing Loss

There are also clinical components which include practical sessions and clinical placements.

Fees: EU students: £2870 f/t; £1435 p/t
      Non-EU students: £9950 f/t only

■ **MSc in Educational Psychology**

This course of professional training in educational psychology is available to experienced teachers.

Length of course: 12 months f/t

Entry requirements: Honours degree in psychology or equivalent recognised by the British Psychological Society.

Course content: The academic components include lectures and seminars on psychological assessment and intervention with children who have special needs, child development, research design and statistics and the role of psychologists in community contexts. Supervised practical work takes place in different Local Education Authority Psychological Services and at the University. Students are also required to write a thesis on an agreed topic relevant to the practice of educational psychology.

Fees: EU students: £9870
      Non-EU students: £14,200

■ **MSc in Profound Learning Disability & Multi-Sensory Impairment**

Length of course: 2 years by distance mode

Entry requirements: Initial relevant degree or qualified professional status.

Course content: Students complete six course units, attend workshops and complete a dissertation.

Fees: £345 per course unit; £210 per course unit distance learning fee

Unless otherwise indicated the following applies to all MEd degrees below:

Length of course: 12 months f/t; 2-5 years p/t

Entry requirement: Degree or equivalent.

■ **MEd in Communications, Education & Technology**

This course is designed to enable teachers, community workers and people working in the media to explore techniques for effective communication within their field of work, with a particular focus on the use of mass media for educational purposes. As well as offering a sound basis in communication theory, this programme of study offers the opportunity to engage in practical project work to produce audio-visual material. Visits to conferences and media organisations can be arranged.

- **MEd in Educational Leadership & School Improvement**

This course is directed to the needs of people who are involved in management and co-ordination of various aspects of the education service. It seeks to combine a practical orientation through the study of: Educational Strategic Planning, Management of Educational Institutions, Management of People in Schools, School Improvement, School Effectiveness.

- **MEd in Educational Psychology**

This course is designed to give teachers and others involved in Education a contemporary view of Educational Psychology as an academic discipline. The degree is recognised by the British Psychological Society as an approved conversion course for trained teachers who wish to apply for 'Graduate Basis for Registration'.

As well as the wide range of course units available from many of the specialist MEd programmes outlined in this section, other options are also available from the Faculty's course list.

- **MEd Further Professional Studies in Hearing Impairment (distance learning)**

Length of course: flexible

Entry requirements: QTS at degree level; an advanced qualification in teaching hearing-impaired children; IELTS score of 7 or equivalent. Applicants from professions other than teaching may be considered for the course providing they have a first degree and relevant knowledge and experience in the field of education for hearing-impaired children.

Course content: Students complete six course units and a dissertation or portfolio which counts for two course units. A majority of the study modules taken and the dissertation or portfolio must be on hearing impairment. A minority of the distance modules produced in the Faculty may be selected with the agreement of the course tutor. It is usually necessary to attend the University for a short period during the study period for the dissertation or portfolio.

Fees: £930 per course unit; £160 per course unit distance learning fee

- **MEd in Information & Communications Technology in Education**

Length of course: 12 months f/t; 2 years p/t

Course content: The course examines all aspects of the use of computers and associated technology in education. There are three main strands: The Computer as Teacher, The Computer as a Tool, Programming Computers. The four compulsory course units are: Computer-assisted Learning, Delivering Learning Materials through the World Wide Web, Learning through Computer Modelling and Simulations Structure, Using Computers to Handle and Communicate Information in Schools and Colleges.

- **MEd in Special & Inclusive Education**

This course is specifically geared to those who are taking, or are aspiring to take, leadership roles in their institutions or services. Consequently it will be particularly relevant to those who are concerned with the development of policy and practice, school organisation, co-ordination and support, including senior and middle managers, special needs co-ordinators, administrators, advisers and those involved in teacher education both in the UK and overseas. Since attention will be given to the developing roles of special provision it will also be of interest to colleagues teaching in special schools and services.

■ MEd in TESOL

Length of course: 12 months f/t (September or January start); 2-5 years p/t
Entry requirements: Applicants should be graduates and trained teachers with 2 to 3 years' full-time language teaching experience.
Course content: The course offers maximum flexibility in content to experienced teachers wishing to study theoretical and practical issues of English language teaching to an advanced level. The modular scheme enables specialists to choose from a variety of options within the ELT field and, more generally, within the wider educational context.

■ MEd in ELT

Length of course: 3-5 years by distance mode (January start)
Entry requirements: Applicants should be graduates and trained teachers with 2 to 3 years' full-time language teaching experience.
Course content: The course offers maximum flexibility in both content and mode of study to experienced teachers wishing to study theoretical and practical issues of ELT to an advanced level. The modular scheme enables specialists to choose from a large variety of options within the ELT field.
Fees: £550 per course unit; £690 for dissertation

■ MEd in Educational Technology & ELT

Length of course: 3-5 years by distance mode (October and April starts)
Entry requirements: Applicants should be graduates and trained teachers with 2 to 3 years' full-time language teaching experience and must have full internet access, including the WWW.
Course content: The course offers maximum flexibility in mode of study to experienced teachers wishing to develop theoretical understanding and practical skills in the use of a wide variety of educational technologies, including computer-assisted language learning, in relation to English language teaching. Students take three core modules and choose a further three modules from the variety of options offered.
Fees: £550 per course unit; £690 for dissertation

■ MEd in Educational Technology & TESOL

Length of course: 12 months f/t; 2-5 years p/t
Entry requirements: Applicants should be graduates and trained teachers with 2 to 3 years full-time language teaching experience.
Course content: The course offers a solid foundation to experienced teachers wishing to develop theoretical understanding and practical skills in the use of a variety of educational technologies, including computer-assisted language learning, in relation to English language teaching. Students take three core course units and choose a further three option course units from the full list available in the Faculty.

RESEARCH DEGREES

- **MPhil / PhD**
- **MSc in Educational Research**
- **EdD**
- **DEdPsy**
- **DCounselling**

The Research and Graduate School enables all the Faculty's research students to become part of a community of educational researchers and to benefit from a free flow of ideas and information. It seeks to ensure that all research students have the best possible support and training in addition to the traditional and highly valued support offered by their supervisors. Its research training programme is recognised by the ESRC for the award of national studentships.

The degrees of *MPhil* and *PhD* are obtainable by research. The wide-ranging interests of the 70 academic staff in the Faculty enable us to offer supervision of research studies over the whole education spectrum from school-based to non-formal and higher education. The international aspect of the Faculty's work over many years and the Faculty's specialist library provide an invaluable resource for research students.

The *MSc in Educational Research* is designed to provide prospective educational researchers with a systematic and wide ranging understanding of theory, methods, techniques and practical research skills.

The *EdD, DEdPsy* and *DCounselling* programmes combine research with taught elements covering new and innovative developments in a named professional field.

Enquiries: The Research and Graduate School, Faculty of Education; janet.grimshaw@man.ac.uk; F: 0161 275 3528

POSTGRADUATE FEES: EU students: £2870 f/t; £1435 p/t
(unless stated otherwise) Non-EU students: £7650f/t; £3825 p/t

Institute of Education at Didsbury
799 Wilmslow Road
Didsbury
MANCHESTER   M20 2RR

Institute of Education at Crewe & Alsager
Crewe Green Road
CREWE CW1 5DU
W: www.mmu.ac.uk

<u>Enquiries and applications:</u> John Wallace, International Office; j.wallace@ mmu.ac.uk;
T: 0161 247 2332/2330; F: 0161 247 6821

BACHELOR DEGREES

■ BEd Hons (4-year)
<u>Length of course:</u> 4 years f/t
<u>Entry requirements:</u> 2 A-levels or equivalent
<u>Course content:</u> Initial teacher training course in Primary Education for teaching children aged 3-11 years.

■ BEd / BEd Hons (2/3-year)
<u>Length of course:</u> 2 or 3 years f/t
<u>Entry requirements:</u> *2-year course:* Higher National qualification or equivalent plus appropriate industrial or commercial experience; *3-year course:* A-levels.
<u>Course content:</u> A course for older students wishing to become teachers of secondary Maths.

■ BEd / BEd Hons (1-year)
<u>Length of course:</u> 1 year f/t
<u>Entry requirements:</u> A diploma or certificate in teaching.
<u>Course content:</u> This is a post-experience qualification for those already qualified as teachers wishing to acquire a degree in Education.

CERTIFICATES / DIPLOMAS

■ PGCE Primary and Secondary
<u>Length of course:</u> 1 year f/t
<u>Entry requirements:</u> Degree or equivalent.
<u>Course content:</u> An initial teacher training qualification for graduates wishing to enter the teaching profession, with a strong emphasis on partnership with schools.
<u>Assessment:</u> Course work and teaching competence.
<u>Fees:</u> *EU students:* £1600; *Non-EU students:* £7000

MASTER'S DEGREES

■ MA / MSc / MEd
A range of part-time Masters programmes are available on a modular basis, including the preparation of a dissertation or thesis. The areas available are:
• Art Education
• Curriculum Management
• Curriculum Studies
• Early Childhood Studies

- Maths Education
- Primary Education
- Science Education
- Special Educational Needs

<u>Length of course:</u> 2-6 years

<u>Entry requirements:</u> An honours degree or equivalent and appropriate teaching experience. With sufficient demand degrees could be offered on a 1-year full-time basis with thesis completion in the following year.

<u>Assessment:</u> By examination and thesis.

<u>Fees:</u> *EU students:* £2540 (f/t); *Non-EU students:* £7000 (f/t)

RESEARCH DEGREES

■ MA/MSc by research, MPhil, PhD

<u>Entry requirements:</u> Honours degree or equivalent.

<u>Research Areas:</u> The Institute of Education is particularly strong in practitioner research with specialist support available in:

- Art Education
- Computer Education
- Early Literacy
- Early Years Education
- Education Management
- Ethnic Studies
- Flexible Learning
- Maths & Science Education
- Outcomes-based Education
- Quality & Evaluation
- Special Educational Needs
- Staff Development

<u>Assessment:</u> By thesis.

<u>Fees:</u> *EU students:* £2540; *Non-EU students:* £6500

OTHER COURSES

■ Tailor-made Courses

Tailor-made courses can be offered in:

- Art & Design Education
- Curriculum Studies
- Early Childhood Studies
- Education & Teaching Studies
- Information Technology
- Maths & Sciences Education
- Primary Education
- Special Educational Needs

■ Programmes in Educational Management

■ Training for School Inspections

Glossary on page XI

School of Lifelong Learning and Education
Trent Park, Bramley Road
Oakwood
LONDON N14 4XS
W: www.lle.mdx.ac.uk

The accreditation of a student's prior learning can be arranged via the Middlesex Scheme enabling students, where appropriate, to enter a degree or postgraduate programme with specific credit at different levels, shortening the length of course.

BACHELOR DEGREES

■ BA Hons Design & Technology
Length of course: 2 years f/t
Entry requirements: HNC/HND or City and Guilds (advanced level) or equivalent
Course content: An initial teacher training qualification. Personal subject development in first year, followed by a 'professional' year.
Enquiries: Peter Taylor; p.taylor@mdx.ac.uk; T: 020 8411 6364

■ BA Hons Primary
Length of course: 3 years f/t
Entry requirements: GCSE English, Maths grade C (those born after 1979 must also have a grade C in a science subject), 2 A-levels at least one of which should be in a National Curriculum Subject, Advanced GNVQ or BTEC National Diploma.
Course content: Initial teacher training course in Primary Education for teaching children 5-11 years with the opportunity to specialise in one subject area.
Enquiries: Debbie Jack; d.jack@mdx.ac.uk; T: 020 8411 6551

CERTIFICATES / DIPLOMAS

■ PGCE Primary and Secondary
Length of course: 1 year f/t
Entry requirements: *Primary:* A first degree, 50% of which should clearly be in a subject or combination of subjects in the National Curriculum; GCSE grade C in Maths and English.
Secondary: Degree or equivalent; GCSE grade C in Maths and English.
Course content: An initial teacher training qualification for graduates wishing to enter the teaching profession with a strong emphasis on partnership with schools.
Subject specialisms:
• Art & Design
• Business Studies
• D&T
• Drama
• English
• Geography
• IT
• Maths

- MFL
- Music
- Science

Enquiries: Joanne Purcell; T: 020 8411 5041

■ **PGCE Secondary Design & Technology (Conversion route)**
Length of course: 2 years f/t
Entry requirements: A first degree or equivalent; relevant aptitude; GCSE grade C or above in Maths and English.
Course content: An initial teacher training qualification. Personal subject development in first year, followed by a professional year with a strong emphasis on partnership with schools.
As D&T is a subject in which there is a shortage of teachers, additional funds are available to support trainees with financial difficulties.
Enquiries: Peter Taylor; p.taylor@mdx.ac.uk; T: 020 8362 6364

MASTER'S DEGREES

- ■ **MA Specific Learning Difficulties**
- ■ **MA Special Educational Needs**
- ■ **MA for Lifelong Learning**

Course content: Continuing Professional Development modular programme for teachers and other professionals.
Enquiries: Judy Lewis; j.a.lewis@mdx.ac.uk; 020 8411 5709

■ **MA / MSc Work-based Learning Studies** (p/t distance learning)
Course content: Work-based Learning Studies involves the identification and recognition of learning gained from work (paid or unpaid) and the use of such learning within individually negotiated programmes of study.
Enquiries: Kathy Doncaster; k.doncaster@mdx.ac.uk; T: 020 8411 5618
Applications: through NCWBLP; T: 020 8411 6118

■ **MProf Work-based Learning Studies** (taught)
Course content: Designed for professionals in business and the professions and designed to recognise postgraduate studies and research carried out within the place of work.
Enquiries: Trevor Corner; t.corner@mdx.ac.uk; T: 020 8411 5618

RESEARCH DEGREES

■ **MPhil, PhD, BPhil**
Entry requirements: Honours degree or equivalent
Research areas: The School has six dedicated Research Centres and offers supervised research in:
- Comparative & International Education
- Technology Education
- IT in Education (especially the use of CD-ROMS)

- Language & Literature Education (particularly argumentation in education and the workplace and children's literature)
- Higher Educational Research
- Learner-managed Learning
- Museum and Gallery Education (especially the use of photography in education and 'visual literacy')
- Primary Education
- Teacher Education
- Specific Learning Difficulties
- SEN
- Contemporary Visual Arts in Education
- Work-based Learning

The School of Lifelong Learning & Education is a central player in a national project to develop and deliver internet-based training aimed at small and medium-sized enterprises (SMEs). It was selected because of its understanding of higher education learning development strategies and its pioneering developments in work-based learning.

Fees: EU students: £3300 f/t; £1800p/t
      Non-EU students: £7500 f/t; £4000 p/t
Enquiries: Trevor Corner; t.corner@mdx.ac.uk; T: 020 8411 5618

■ **DProf Work-based Learning Studies** (taught)
Course content: Designed for professionals in business and the professions and designed to recognise postgraduate studies and research carried out within the place of work.
Enquiries: Trevor Corner; t.corner@mdx.ac.uk; T: 020 8411 5618

OTHER COURSES

■ **Short Courses**
- Professional Development for Teachers
- Postgraduate Certificate in Education in
  - Leadership & Management
  - Teaching & Learning
  - Social Inclusion
Enquiries: Vicki Macleod; v.macleod@mdx.ac.uk

UNIVERSITY OF NEWCASTLE

Centre for International Studies in Education (CISE) T: 0191 222 6377
Faculty of Education   F: 0191 222 5691
St Thomas Street   E: cise-education@ncl.ac.uk
NEWCASTLE UPON TYNE   NE1 7RU   W: www.ncl.ac.uk/cise

Dean of Faculty: Dr Gerry J Docherty
Director of CISE: Ms Sue Robson

The Faculty of Education comprises:
• The Department of Education
• The Department of Speech
• The Centre for International Studies in Education (CISE)
• The Centre for Lifelong Learning

The *Centre for International Studies in Education* was established in 1958. The Centre provides daytime full-time taught courses of further study and opportunities for research for teachers, teacher trainers, headteachers, advisers, inspectors and planners who are concerned with nursery, primary and/or secondary schooling, the training of teachers, special schools or units, educational planning, monitoring and evaluation, school inspection and advisory services, educational supervision and management. Courses are designed to reflect international perspectives and over the years participants have come from the majority of the world's countries.

The general aim of all courses is to familiarise students with current developments in Education. Students are encouraged to identify key areas of planning and practice and to develop their special interests, giving consideration to national objectives and the needs and interests of the learners who are their concern. In this way CISE seeks to enable teachers, teacher trainers and advisers to develop their own potential and to make effective contributions to the development of their own educational systems.

Course directors for the areas of specialism are as follows:
• Guidance & Counselling: Ms Sue Pattison
• Educational Management: Dr David Mercer
• Special Educational Needs: Ms Sue Robson
• TESOL: Ms Tina Lausevic

Taught courses are followed mainly during the day (9.00-16.30). Tutors have extensive experience in countries other than Britain.

Good accommodation is available in University halls of residence and self-catering flats which are within a short walking distance of the School of Education. Students may rent private accommodation if they wish.

In addition to the University Library and University Computing Services (all CISE students register as computer users), there are good facilities for indoor and outdoor sport and leisure activities.

The University Language Centre provides programmes for students who wish to improve their English before they start their studies at the University. In addition, a variety of courses in English for academic purposes are provided by the Language Centre throughout the year.

BACHELOR DEGREES

■ BPhil in Educational Studies

Length of course: 1 calendar year f/t (October - September)

Entry requirements: QTS; appropriate experience; IELTS score of 5.0.

Course content: The BPhil(Ed) is a first degree for qualified teachers from the UK and other countries. Courses in four specialist areas of study are available (see below). Students attend lectures and seminars on practice and theory related to their special area of study and are given many opportunities to consider the relevance of current ideas to their own educational context. The aim of the course is to strengthen professional skills to enable educators to become effective participants in change.

Assessment: Assignments and a dissertation of about 12-15,000 words.

■ BPhil(Ed) in Educational Management

The course is suitable for those who hold management positions in schools or other educational institutions as well as for experienced teachers who wish to prepare for positions of responsibility.

■ BPhil(Ed) in Guidance & Counselling in Education

The course is suitable for those for whom counselling is part of their professional lives and who wish to become more skilful helpers with students, staff and parents in educationally related settings.

■ BPhil(Ed) in Special Educational Needs

The course is suitable for those who have experience working with children with special educational needs as well as those who wish to specialise in the needs of children with learning difficulties in mainstream classes.

■ BPhil(Ed) in TESOL

The course is suitable for English language specialists who wish to develop their understanding of the theory and practice of language teaching. A TESOL for Young Learners option is also available.

Specialist brochures detailing modules in each of these areas are available on request. See also the CISE website (www.ncl.ac.uk/cise).

CERTIFICATES / DIPLOMAS

■ Postgraduate Certificate/Diploma in Advanced Educational Studies

Length of course: Certificate: 4 months f/t; Diploma: 8 months f/t

Entry requirements: QTS; appropriate experience; first degree; IELTS of 6.5.

Course content: Both degrees are available in: TESOL, Educational Management, Special Educational Needs, Guidance & Counselling.

Fees: Certificate: one-third of f/t yearly fees; Diploma: two-thirds of f/t yearly fees

MASTER'S DEGREES

■ MEd

The MEd course is open to well-qualified and experienced teachers, heads of schools, teacher trainers, advisers and inspectors who meet the entry requirements. The aim of the MEd is to develop professional skills to enable educators to become effective

managers of change.
Length of course: 1 calendar year f/t (October to September)
Entry requirements: QTS; appropriate experience; first degree; IELTS score of 6.5.
Suitable candidates who do not hold a first degree should take the BPhil first, thus taking a 2-year route to the MEd *(see Bachelor Degrees above)*.
Course content: The course includes taught elements, seminars and may include placements in appropriate educational institutions.
Assessment: Assignments and a research dissertation of 15,000-20,000 words.
For large groups the MEd is also available in a two-year format taught entirely overseas by Newcastle lecturers. Currently the course is being delivered in the United Arab Emirates and Hong Kong. Further details on request.

■ MEd Special Educational Needs
This course is suitable for those who have experience working with children with special educational needs, as well as those who wish to specialise in the needs of children with learning difficulties in mainstream classes.

■ MEd Educational Management
This course is suitable for those who hold management positions in schools or other educational institutions, as well as for experienced teachers who wish to prepare for positions of responsibility.

■ MEd Guidance & Counselling in Education
This course is designed for practising or aspiring professionals from a range of professions who wish to promote a critical understanding of counselling frameworks as well as developing practical counselling skills.

■ MEd TESOL
This course is suitable for English Language Teaching specialists who wish to develop their understanding of the theory and practice of language teaching. A *TESOL for Young Learners* option is also available.

■ MA in Media Technology for TESOL
This course is suitable for English Language Teaching specialists who wish to learn how to use computer video technology effectively in the classroom.

RESEARCH DEGREES

■ Integrated PhD in Education
Length of course: 3 years f/t
Entry requirements: QTS; appropriate experience; first degree; IELTS of 6.5.
Course content: The new PhD in Education is a partly taught doctorate. Candidates take a range of taught, assessed modules and write a research thesis of 40-50,000 words.
Enquiries: Dr Paul Seedhouse, CISE *(see beginning of entry for contact details);* W: www.ncl.ac.uk/integratedphd

FEES (for all programmes)   EU students: £2865
                                 Non-EU students: £7185

School of Education
Caerleon Campus
PO Box 101
NEWPORT NP18 3YH

T: 01633 432432
F: 01633 432850
E: uic@newport.ac.uk
W: www.newport.ac.uk

Head of Department: Dr Carl Peters
Enquiries: University Information Centre

UWCN's teacher education programmes are based at the attractive Caerleon campus, which overlooks the historic Roman town of Caerleon, just a few miles upstream from Newport itself. With excellent road and rail links, Newport is easily accessible from all parts of the UK. Student accommodation is available on the campus, including modern en-suite rooms.

BACHELOR DEGREES

■ **BA Hons Design & Technology with QTS**
Length of course: 3 years
Entry requirements: 2 A-levels, 12-unit VCE, BTEC National Diploma or GNVQ Level 3 with passes in Maths and English and one other subject at GCSE or O-level or equivalent (should be relevant to D&T).
Course content: Strong emphasis on practical issues; includes 24 weeks of school-based study.
Assessment: Course work, including projects, written examinations and practical teaching competence.

■ **BA Hons Primary Studies with QTS**
Length of course: 3 years
Entry requirements: 2 A-levels, 12-unit VCE, BTEC National Diploma or GNVQ Level 3 with passes in Maths and English (and Science for candidates born on or after 1 Sept. 1979) and one other subject at GCSE or O-level or equivalent.
Course content: Includes 24 weeks of school-based study. Students choose one of the following subjects to study in greater depth: Art, English, D&T, Geography, History, Maths, Music, PE, RE, Science, Welsh.
Assessment: Course work, written examinations and practical teaching competence.

■ **BSc Education: Design & Technology**
■ **BSc Design & Technology with ICT**
■ **BSc Education: Maths with ICT**
■ **BSc Education: Maths with Science**
Length of course: 2 years
Entry requirements: Candidates must be over 21 (by 1 October of year of entry), have GCSE passes in English and Maths, or have achieved equivalent standard, and have completed at least one year of higher education in the appropriate subject or subjects.
Course content: Includes 24 weeks of school-based study.
Assessment: Course work, including projects, written examinations and practical teaching competence.

CERTIFICATES / DIPLOMAS / MASTER'S DEGREES

■ PGCE Primary

Length of course: 1 year

Entry requirements: Degree or equivalent; English Language, Maths (and Science for candidates born on or after 1 Sept. 1979) passes at GCSE or equivalent.

Course content: Core and foundation curriculum subjects, teaching studies, primary studies workshop and block school experience.

Assessment: Course work and practical teaching competence.

■ PGCE Design & Technology

Length of course: 1 year

Entry requirements: Degree or equivalent in a relevant subject; English Language and Maths passes at GCSE or equivalent.

Course content: 12 weeks university-based study, 24 weeks school-based study.

Assessment: Course work, written examinations and practical teaching competence.

■ PGCE Information & Communications Technology

Length of course: 1 year

Entry requirements: Degree or equivalent in a subject related to ICT; English Language and Maths passes at GCSE or equivalent.

Course aims: To prepare graduates to teach ICT in secondary schools (11-18) and to support the teaching of other subjects using ICT.

Course structure/content: 12 weeks university-based study, 24 weeks school-based study. Modules include:
• ICT in a Social Context
• Learning & Teaching with ICT
• Issues in Teaching & Learning with ICT

Assessment: Coursework, including essays, projects and portfolio; practical teaching competence.

■ PGCE Post-Compulsory Education & Training

Length of course: 1 year

Entry requirements: Degree or equivalent.

Course aims: To prepare graduates to teach in the post-compulsory (16+) sector, eg further and adult education, leisure and youth work and training personnel.

Course structure/content: 16 week teaching practice; 18 weeks university-based study. Core modules:
• Preparing to Teach
• Assessment of Learning
• Teaching & Learning Strategies
Options include:
• Guidance & Counselling
• Special Needs
• Learning Technologies

Assessment: Coursework assignments; practical teaching competence.

- **MA/Diploma/Certificate in Education**
- **MA/Diploma/Certificate in Special Educational Needs**

Length of course: 2-5 years p/t

Entry requirements: Candidates under 25 must have an initial degree or equivalent. Candidates over 25 without a degree may apply for entry if they have held a position of responsibility in a relevant field for at least two years.

Course content: In both courses, students can choose from a wide range of modules. They must successfully complete two to obtain the certificate, four to gain the diploma, and four plus a dissertation for the MA. In certain modules there may also be a teaching practice requirement.

Assessment: Continuous assessment in each module.

Fees: EU students: £405 per module; £305 dissertation
    Non-EU students: *see fees below*

FEES

EU students: £1100
Non-EU students: £6700 undergraduate; £7200 post-graduate

UNIVERSITY OF NORTH LONDON

School of Education
166-220 Holloway Road
LONDON   N7 8DB

T: 020 7753 5104
F: 020 7753 5400
E: j.kazemzadeh@unl.ac.uk
W: www.unl.ac.uk

Head of School: Professor Jon Davison

BACHELOR DEGREES

■ **BEd (International)**
Length of course: 1 year f/t
Entry requirements: Diploma or degree in Education; candidates with at least three years of teaching experience will be considered.
Course content: This course has been designed specifically for teachers from overseas who wish to improve their qualifications through the study of Education. Some units are taken alongside home students, others are taught separately. There is a strong focus on practitioner research. As well as providing opportunities for reflection and analysis of the students' experience in their home setting, the course provides opportunities for the study of primary education in England, particularly in urban contexts.
Fees: £5990
Enquiries: Gill Venn; g.venn@unl.ac.uk

■ **BA Hons Education Studies**
Length of course: 3 years f/t; also p/t
Entry requirements: Normal University Entrance requirements or equivalent. For mature students other qualifications or experience may be considered.
Course content: This degree can be taken as a Major, Joint or Minor part of the Humanities Modular Degree Scheme. The subject is treated as a distinctive academic area, using a variety of theoretical perspectives and emphasising the processes of teaching and learning in a wide variety of contexts. The interdisciplinary approach is a special feature of the course and consists of four fields of study:
• Cognitive Studies
• Cultural Studies
• Political Economy Studies
• Historical and Philosophical Studies
All students take two core methodological units and a double placement unit which can be in any location where issues of teaching and learning can be considered.
Fees: ca £5990 pa (f/t)
Enquiries: Chris Richards; c.richards@unl.ac.uk

■ **BA Hons Early Childhood Studies**
    See CERTIFICATES / DIPLOMAS below.

CERTIFICATES / DIPLOMAS

■ **Certificate/Diploma in Higher Education (Early Childhood Studies Scheme)**
Length of course: 1-9 years p/t by distance learning
Entry requirements: Substantial experience of working with young children in the age group 0-8. Entry is at the discretion of the University of North London.

Course content: Studying through the Early Childhood Scheme can lead to:
• Certificate in HE (8 modules)
• Diploma in HE (16 modules)
• BA Hons Early Childhood (24 modules)
The aim of the scheme is to build on students' experience and link theory to practice. A wide selection of modules maximises the scope for individual development. Students work through a module pack while keeping in touch with a regional tutor who gives feedback on progress. Work is assessed at the University of North London and detailed feedback given.
Fees: £500 per module
Enquiries: Linda Pound; l.pound@unl.ac.uk

■ **PGDip in Education**
See MA Education below.

MASTER'S DEGREES

■ **MA Education**
Length of course: 1 year f/t; 2-7 years p/t
Entry requirements: Honours degree in an appropriate subject.
Course content: Six taught modules include two compulsory core units:
• Local & National Issues in Education
• Curriculum Studies
MA descriptors include:
• Language & Literature in Education
• Primary Maths Education
• Management in Education
• Early Childhood Education
A double unit dissertation of 15,000 words completes the programme.
It is also possible to combine Education with other pathways in the Humanities and Education Postgraduate Scheme (Modern European Studies, Modern Drama Studies, Representation and Modernity).
This programme can also lead to a Postgraduate Diploma in Education.
Fees: £5990 (f/t)
Enquiries: Pam Wadsworth; p.wadswortha@unl.ac.uk

■ **MA TEFL**
Length of course: 1 year
Entry requirements: Normally a first degree, a language teaching qualification and some experience in teaching or a related field.
Course content: The framework of the course is modular, consisting of five taught modules, two project modules and a unique placement module where participants have the opportunity to gain experience and explore new ideas in a professional environment. An optional language studies workshop is also offered. The modules cover areas such as:

- Current Issues in ELT
- Assessment & Testing
- Managing Global Change in ELT
- Multimedia Materials Design
- Language Teaching Methodology

Fees: £6350

Enquiries: Tim Marr; t.marr@unl.ac.uk

■ **MRes Research Methods in Education**

Length of course: 1 year f/t; 2-7 years p/t

Entry requirements: A good honours degree

Course content: This modular programme prepares students for engaging in their own educational research or to act as consumers/commissioners of research. It is part of a University-wide research methods programme and some courses are taken with students in other disciplines. Modules cover issues in research methodology, including the use of qualitative and quantitative approaches, philosophical issues and contemporary issues in educational research. A dissertation forms 60% of the course. The MRes may be combined with the MA in Education Studies.

Fees: ca £5990 (f/t)

Enquiries: Linda Mulcahy

RESEARCH DEGREES

■ **MPhil, PhD**

Length of course: MPhil: 2-5 years f/t; 3-7 years p/t

PhD: 3-6 years f/t; 4-9 years p/t

Course content/structure: These research degrees are based upon the presentation of a thesis (MPhil 40,000 words, PhD 80,000 words). Students enrol with the university and after some six months present detailed research proposals to the Research Degrees Committee for formal registration for either an MPhil, an MPhil with the possibility of conversion to a PhD or a PhD direct. Students are guided to take related programmes of study to assist them in their research and a programme of suitable modules is available. The School of Education has particular research interests in:

- Primary School Curriculum (particularly Children's Social and Economic Education, Maths Education and Language Learning)
- Home-school Links
- Truancy
- Primary Education in Cyprus

It is possible for overseas students normally resident in their own country to study on a part-time basis provided that sufficient visits are made to London and the supervisor visits the student's own country. This is normally six weeks a year.

Fees: ca £5990 pa f/t; ca £1900 pa p/t

Enquiries: Merryn Hutchings; m.hutchings@unl.ac.uk

University of Northumbria at Newcastle
Faculty of Health, Social Work and Education
Coach Lane Campus
NEWCASTLE UPON TYNE NE7 7XA

T: 0191 215 6336
F: 0191 215 6010
E: julie.cafferty@unn.ac.uk
W: www.unn.ac.uk

Enquiries: Admissions

The University of Northumbria at Newcastle offers a wide range of pre- and post-qualifying courses and research degree awards. Pre-qualifying courses are normally full-time and post-qualifying part-time.

BACHELOR DEGREES

■ BA Hons Primary Education
Length of course: 3 years f/t
Course content: The course prepares for teaching in the 3-11 age range with an emphasis in the Early Years. The programme covers all areas of the primary curriculum.

■ BA or BA Hons Professional Practice in Education
Length of course: 1 year p/t
The course is offered either as evening sessions or as blocks of 3 to 4 days with tutorial and group workshop support.
Entry requirements: Applicants should be practitioners who are already qualified teachers, educators or trainers.
Course content: Course members team to systematically reflect on their practice, collecting and analysing data to inform their professional duties and plan some developments of their approach. They implement their plan and monitor its effects through a process of Action Research and Enquiry.
Assessment: Two substantial written reports.

■ BA Equestrian and Teaching Studies with BHS Status (Assistant Instructor)
The University of Northumbria, Northumberland College (Kirkley Hall Campus) and East Durham and Houghall Community College are working together to offer this new degree which is currently awaiting validation by the University of Northumbria and the British Horse Society.
Length of course: 3 years f/t
Entry requirements: 220 tariff points, five GCSEs at grade C or above (including English, Maths, Science).
Course structure/aims: There are two major strands to this course:
- The Equestrian Studies strand will be based on the British Horse Society's examination syllabus working towards stage 4.
- The Teaching Studies strand will aim to produce a graduate who will be a proficient teacher within the context of equestrianism.

Assessment: Practical ridden and horse management examinations; assignments, portfolios and presentations; teaching practice.
Enquiries: T: 0191 215 6333; F: 0191 215 6404; E: hs.admissions@northumbria.ac.uk

CERTIFICATES / DIPLOMAS

■ **PGCE Primary**

A school-based programme for graduates preparing for the 3-8 or 7-11 range.
Length of course: 1 year (38 weeks) f/t

■ **Modular Primary PGCE**

This modular course is for ICT-literate graduates with a degree relevant to the childrens'
National Curriculum who have easy access to a computer and Internet connection.
The course is delivered by distance learning with some residential parts and two
assessed placements (the first of four, the second of six weeks).
Length of course: 1 year

MASTER'S DEGREES

■ **MA Learning in Schools**

This course is designed for experienced educational practitioners.
Length of course: 1 year f/t
Entry requirements: A first degree or equivalent, preferably education or social science
related; a minimum of two years' full-time teaching experience of pupils aged 5-18.
Course aims: A key intention of the course is to establish the conditions and standards for rigorous critical enquiry and discourse. Participants meet with practitioners
with varied experiences of schooling and who work within systems where the under-
lying values, practices and ethos may be very different to those with which the participant is most familiar.
Course content: Participants focus on practices in educational systems with particular
reference to national policies and their impact on learning. The course creates conditions in which participants consider the implications of what they learn for policy and
practice in their own professional context.
Assessment: Five assessed units. Assessed work forms an integral part of the teaching
and learning requirements; there are no examinations.
Enquiries: Colven Gibson; colven.gibson@unn.ac.uk; T: 0191 215 6461

■ **MA Early Years Education and Care**

Length of course: 3-5 years
Entry requirements: Normally graduate status or equivalent.
Course aims: This course gives an opportunity for early years practitioners to under-
take systematic enquiry into their settings, which will enable them to lead change
based on a theoretical framework.
Course content: Units in
• Teaching & Learning
• Management & Leadership in the Early Years
• Home & School Links
• Special Educational Needs in the Early Years
• Four research units
Assessment: Eight assignments and a dissertation.
Enquiries: Paul Lunn; paul.lunn@unn.ac.uk

RESEARCH DEGREES

■ **MPhil, PhD**

We welcome full and part-time proposals for research-based programmes that feature an examination of:

• Practice Development in Classrooms
• Organisational Change
• School & Staff Development

OTHER COURSES

■ **Short Courses / Individual Study Programmes**

Short courses and individual study programmes may be designed specifically to meet the particular needs of overseas educationalists. Similarly, students from overseas may wish to follow individual modules of existing programmes and gain credit.

UNIVERSITY OF NOTTINGHAM

I. School of Education
Jubilee Campus
NOTTINGHAM   NG8 1BB

T: 0115 951 4543
F: 0115 846 6600
W: www.nottingham.ac.uk/education

Head of School: Dr Carol Hall
Enquiries: The Enquiries Secretary; education-enquiries@nottingham.ac.uk

The School of Education is situated on a new purpose-built complex, just three miles from the centre of Nottingham. It is a major provider and facilitator of in-service and pre-service education and training for teachers and other educators and an internationally recognised centre for research, curriculum and professional development and training. The School has a tradition of welcoming applications from those working in education who do not possess conventional academic qualifications but can demonstrate relevant experience and abilities.

BACHELOR DEGREES

- **BEd Hons**

Length of course: 1 year f/t (after satisfactory completion of a preliminary course)
Entry requirements: Certificate in Education at an appropriate level, plus appropriate teaching experience.

MASTER'S DEGREES

All Master's level programmes are also offered at Diploma level.

- **MA in Children's Literature**

Length of course: 2 years p/t

- **MA in Teaching Content through a Foreign Language**

Length of course: 2 years p/t
Also available in our International Summer School (2-4 years p/t).

- **MA in Continuing Professional Development and School Improvement**

Length of course: 1year f/t; 2 years p/t
Also available in our International Summer School (2-4 years p/t).

- **MA in Counselling Studies**

Length of course: 1year f/t; 2 years p/t

- **MA in Educational Leadership**

Length of course: 2-4 years p/t (also available in our International Summer School)

- **MA in English Language Teacher Development**

Length of course: 1 year f/t

- **MA in English Language Teaching**

Length of course: 1 year f/t; 2 years p/t
Also available in our International Summer School (2-4 years p/t).

- **MA in Human Relations**

Length of course: 1 year f/t; 2 years p/t

- **MA in Special Needs**
Length of course: 1 year f/t; 2 years p/t

- **MA in Teaching**
Length of course: 3-4 years p/t

CERTIFICATES / DIPLOMAS / MASTER'S DEGREES

- **PGCE**
Length of course: 36 weeks f/t, starting mid-September

- **Modular PGCE**
Length of course: to be completed within 3 years

RESEARCH DEGREES

- **MPhil / PhD**
Length of course: MPhil: 2 years f/t (min); 4 years p/t
PhD: 3 years f/t (min); 6 years p/t

- **EdD in Educational Leadership** (taught doctorate in Education)
Length of course: 2 years f/t; 4 years p/t

- **EdD in Teacher Education** (taught doctorate in Education)
Length of course: 2 years f/t; 4 years p/t

- **EdD in Literacy** (taught doctorate in Education)
Length of course: 2 years f/t; 4 years p/t

II. School of Continuing Education
  Jubilee Campus
  NOTTINGHAM   NG8 1BB

T: 0115 846 6466
F: 0115 951 3711
E: ce-enquiries@nottingham.ac.uk
W: www.nottingham.ac.uk/continuing-education

Head of School: Peter Preston
Enquiries: Student Administration Office

CERTIFICATES / DIPLOMAS

■ Postgraduate Certificate in Continuing Education

This is both an initial teacher training course in the adult education sector and a programme suitable for inservice development. It is suitable for those working in further and higher education as well as those in community projects, health and nursing education and trainers in the public services.

This programme is part of the DfES pilot training salaries scheme for initial teacher training in the further education sector.

Length of course: 1 year f/t; 2 years p/t

Entry requirements: Normally Bachelor's degree or equivalent.

Course structure: The course consists of eight compulsory modules, one of which is supervised teaching practice. There is a progression route to the MA in Lifelong Education.

Assessment: Assignments, presentations and supervised teaching practice.

Fees: EU students: £1100 f/t; £550 p/t
      Non-EU students: £7520 f/t; £3760 p/t

MASTER'S DEGREES

■ MA/Diploma in Lifelong Education

Length of course: 1 year f/t; 2 years p/t

Entry requirements: A second-class honours degree or higher or equivalent qualifications/experience.

Course structure: The course has four Common Core modules which cover theoretical perspectives on:
• Adult Learning
• Policy Issues
• Management Issues
• Research Methods

The course has four specialist strands:
• Adult Basic Skills
• Learning & Teaching
• Comparative & International
• Management

These are designated by the choice of one Specialist Core module and the dissertation (the latter for MA students only). In addition, all students choose one elective module on topics such as:
• European Systems of Vocational Education & Training

- Human Rights in Education
- Philosophical Issues
- Non-formal Education & Development

Assessments: Each module is assessed by 5000 words or equivalent; for MA students only: dissertation of 15,000-20,000 words.

Fees: EU students: £2870 f/t; £1300 p/t
      Non-EU students: £7520 f/t; £3760 p/t

RESEARCH DEGREES

■ MPhil, PhD

Entry requirements: Bachelor's degree or equivalent with first or second class honours, or higher degree.

Course content: Supervision in the following broad research areas is available:
- Adult Teaching & Learning
- Continuing Education & Social Exclusion
- Access & Disability
- Further & Higher Education
- Comparative Education & Development
- Human Capital Development
- Training & Economic & Social Regeneration
- Adult Education & the Arts

Potential applicants are encouraged to contact the Programme Director to discuss their research ideas before submitting an application.

Fees: EU students: £2870 f/t; £1300 p/t
      Non-EU students: £7520 f/t; £3760 p/t

■ EdD in Lifelong Education (taught doctorate)

Entry requirements: Master's degree or equivalent together with a minimum of two years' relevant professional experience.

Course content/structure: Module specialisms in:
- Models of Adult Teaching & Learning
- Management of Change in Lifelong Education
- The Political Economy of Education: Comparative Perspectives
- Theory, Method & Application of Research in Lifelong Education

The programme is timetabled in week-long blocks at half term and there is an annual research summer school. The programme may also be available on a two-centre basis for approved groups of overseas applicants.

Assessment: Assignments and thesis of 40,000-50,000 words (supervision is provided)

Fees: EU students: £2870 f/t; £1300 p/t
      Non-EU students: £7520 f/t; £3760 p/t

Faculty of Education
Ada Byron King Building
Clifton
NOTTINGHAM NG11 8NS

T: 0115 848 6711
F: 0115 848 6747
E: edu.admissions@ntu.ac.uk
W: www.education.ntu.ac.uk

Dean of Faculty: Professor Nigel Hastings

BACHELOR DEGREES

■ **BA Hons Primary Education**

The aim of this course is to develop skilled professionals with the expertise to undertake the challenging and rewarding role of primary teacher.

The Department of Primary Education is based in brand new, purpose-build accommodation on the University's Clifton Campus, adjacent to the student village, shops and the Clifton library. Built and equipped to the highest standards, this new building gives Primary Education students and staff access to the latest resources in a totally modern environment.

Length of course: 4 years

Course content: Candidates choose from one of two routes: Early Years (age 3-8) or Primary (age 5-11). Students have regular contact with local schools and learn about research and practice in education. For *Primary students*, particular importance is given to the teaching of the UK Primary Core Curriculum. Students develop particular strength in two subjects - one from the core curriculum and one from the UK Primary Foundation Curriculum. For *Early Years students*, the focus is one the UK Foundation Stage Curriculum.

Enquiries: Cynthia Ridgley

■ **BSc Hons Design & Technology Education**

This course prepares D&T teachers for the secondary phase (training age 11-18).

Length of course: 4 years; a degree is available after 3 years for those who subsequently decide on an alternative career to teaching or an alternative PGCE route into teaching.

Course content: Professional studies and school experience are included in most years but are concentrated into Year 4. A short period of industrial placement is included in Year 2.

Enquiries: Cynthia Ridgley

For the following courses please enquire for details:

■ **BSc Hons Business & Information Communications Technology**
■ **BA Hons Psychology & Educational Development**
■ **BA Hons Business, Leisure & Sports Education**

Enquiries: Jean Ellis

CERTIFICATES / DIPLOMAS

- **PGCert in Education Primary (age 5-11)**

Length of course: 38 weeks f/t within a 10-month period (mid-September to end of June/mid July)

Entry requirements: BA, BSc

Course content: All course members explore the nature of teaching and learning through a variety of contexts including school experiences, workshops, lectures, seminars and personal study. By a process of reflection, analysis and evaluation each student is supported in developing a coherent critical approach to their work as a classroom teacher. The course aims to foster appropriate attitudes towards professional responsibilities.

Course members follow curriculum courses concerned with teaching the primary age-range in the UK National Curriculum core subjects of Maths, Science and English plus D&T, ICT, PE & Movement, Art, History, Geography, RE, Music.

Roughly half of the course involves work in schools and teachers are closely concerned with the ongoing planning and development of a partnership approach linking school and university.

Enquiries: Kathryn Whitt

- **PGCert in Education Secondary (age 11-18)**

Length of course: 36 weeks f/t within a 10-month period (mid-September to end of June)

Entry requirements: BA, BSc or professional qualification recognised as being of UK degree equivalence.

Course content: All students will study the teaching of a main subject chosen from Business Education, D&T, English, ICT, Maths or Science (Biology, Chemistry, and Physics).

The course aims to develop:

- An understanding of the place of the secondary school of the specialist subjects in relation to the National Curriculum.
- An understanding of the challenges involved in the teaching and learning of these subjects across the full ability range normally encountered in secondary schools.
- The understanding, skills and personal qualities necessary to teaching the specialist subjects to secondary school pupils.
- The understanding, skills and personal qualities necessary for class management and control.
- The understanding, skills and personal qualities relevant to membership of a school staff and of the teaching profession.

The course includes 24 weeks of school experience.

Enquiries: Kathryn Whitt

- **Professional Development in Education Programme**

Enquiries: Sue Brewill

RESEARCH DEGREES

■ MPhil, PhD in Education

Graduates with appropriate qualifications and experience are invited to apply for a full-time or part-time research project leading either to the MPhil degree or the PhD. The Faculty of Education aims:

- To influence educational practice and policy through informing educational decisions and improving practice.
- To develop a strong reputation for high quality research both externally and internally.
- To define and develop clear and distinctive areas of knowledge and expertise.

The Faculty has prominent and lively groups of researchers in the following areas:

- Developing Primary Practice - especially Class Management and Curriculum Specialisms (Art, Science, Maths, Language).
- Education for Work - Partnership, Business Education, Key Skills.
- Social Justice & Differentiation - especially Entitlement, Access, Development/Environmental Issues.
- Learning & Teaching in Higher Education - Distance Education, Reflective Practice, Supervision and Assessment.

Applicants may select a focus for their project, preferably with links with one of the above areas, and propose a line of research which is appropriate to their own qualifications and experience. While many students teach in schools or colleges, others come from a range of different professional backgrounds. Applicants who are unable to live in the Nottingham area would be required to have easy access to speedy and reliable methods of communication such as fax and e-mail and to make arrangements to visit the University on a regular basis. Applications can be received by the University at any time in the academic year.

<u>Enquiries:</u> Professor Morwenna Griffiths

Faculty of Education & Language Studies
Walton Hall
MILTON KEYNES   MK7 6AA

T: 01908 652150
F: 01908 652187
E: a.j.nightingale@open.ac.uk
W: www.open.ac.uk/education

Contact Person: Adam Nightingale, Marketing

The Faculty of Education & Language Studies at The Open University provides a diverse range of courses and qualifications for education professionals as well as for those with a general interest in education. The Open University has developed a unique approach to supported open learning over the past 30 years which allows students to continue working whilst they are studying our courses. The Faculty of Education & Language Studies provides materials, assessment and tutorial support for students in Western Europe. From 2002, our MA in Education/MEd (Applied Linguistics) will be available worldwide (excluding Singapore and the USA).This consists of three Masters modules: E841, E844 and EZX836.

Our courses are taught and assessed in the English language, so students will need a level of proficiency that allows them to communicate effectively at the chosen level of study.

BACHELOR DEGREES

- **E123 Working with Children in the Early Years**
- **E124 Supporting Childrens' Learning in the Early Years**
- **ED209 Child Development**
- **U210 English Language: Past, Present & Future**
- **U212 Childhood**
- **E242 Learning for All**
- **E300 English Language & Literacy**

Length of courses: 9 months p/t (February to October)
Entry requirements: none
Assessment: Assignments and examination (the number of assignments varies with each course)

- **Undergraduate Diploma in English Language Studies**

Awarded after successful completion of both U210 and E300 *(see above).*

CERTIFICATES / DIPLOMAS

- **Advanced Diploma in Child Development**
- **Advanced Diploma in Language & Literacy**
- **Advanced Diploma in Special Needs in Education**
- **Advanced Diploma in TESOL**

Length of courses: 2 years p/t (February to October)
Entry requirements: none
Course content: Advanced Diplomas consist of an undergraduate level course and a postgraduate level course.
Assessment: Assignments and examinations.

Glossary on page XI

■ **PGCert in the Co-ordination of Special Education Provision**
Length of course: 9 months p/t
Entry requirements: First degree or equivalent and some experience in a field of education. Access to an Educational Institution is also required.
Course content: The course consists of one Masters module: E831 Professional Development for Special Education Needs Co-ordinators.
Assessment: Assignments and a project.

■ **PGCE**
Length of course: 6 months to 3 years, p/t, f/t or a mixture of both.
Entry requirements: A degree or equivalent relevant to your chosen subject; English Language and Mathematics at O-level or GCSE grade C or above; to be over the age of 21 at the start of the course.
Course structure: We carry out an individual Needs Analysis which recognises your prior learning and experience and leads to an individually tailored route to qualified teacher status.
Course content: The following Secondary subjects are offered:
• D&T
• Geography
• Mathematics
• MFL (French, German, Spanish)
• Music
• Science
Assessment: Assignments and a project.

MASTER'S DEGREES

■ **MA in Education**
Length of course: normally 9 months p/t (February to October) for each 60-point module. MA in Education qualification is 180 points.
Entry requirements: First degree or equivalent and some experience in a field of education.
Course content: A choice of 15 modules.
Assessment: Assignments and examination or project (the number of assignments varies with each module).

FEES vary according to the level of the course and to the location of the student. Details are given in the *Professional Development in Education* prospectus (available from above address) and on our website.

Department of Educational Studies
15 Norham Gardens
OXFORD OX2 6PY

T: 01865 274024
F: 01865 274027
E: rosalind.gerring@educational-studies.ox.ac.uk
W: http://units.ox.ac.uk/departments/edstud

Head of Department: Professor Richard Pring
Enquiries: Secretary for Higher Degree Courses

MASTER'S DEGREES

- **MSc Educational Research Methodology**
- **MSc Comparative and International Studies**

Length of courses: 1 year f/t
Entry requirements: Good honours degree or equivalent.
Assessment: Written examination; 15,000 - 20,000 word dissertation.

- **MSc Applied Linguistics and Second Language Acquisition**

Length of courses: 1 year f/t; 2 years p/t
Entry requirements: Good honours degree or equivalent.
Assessment: Examination at the end of each module; 25,000-word (max) dissertation.

RESEARCH DEGREES

- **DPhil**

Entry requirements: Good honours degree or equivalent.
Research areas:
- Teaching, Learning & Teacher Development
- Educational Policy
- Families, Early Learning & Literacy
- Comparative & International Education

Assessment: Research training (1 year); submission of thesis of 100,000 words (max), normally after two more years.

FEES

EU students: £2740
Non-EU students: £6851
College fees: ca. £1800

OXFORD BROOKES UNIVERSITY

Westminster Institute of Education
Harcourt Hill Campus
OXFORD OX2 9AT

T: 01865 741111
F: 01865 488484
E: query@brookes.ac.uk
W: www.brookes.ac.uk/schools/education

Head of Institute: Dr David Langford
Enquiries: Dr Cliff Marshall, Senior Tutor, Admissions and Recruitment
Prospectus: Call 01865 484848

The Institute of Education has approximately 2000 full- and part-time students and offers a comprehensive range of courses at both undergraduate and postgraduate level, together with specialist short courses and consultancy services tailored to the needs of clients.

The Institute is sited on the university's Harcourt Hill campus, overlooking Oxford and within easy reach of the city centre.

The Institute has considerable expertise in the provision of initial training and continuing professional development and has been awarded substantial TTA funds for in-service work covering the period of 2001/02 to 2003/04.

BACHELOR DEGREES

■ BA Primary Initial Teacher Education

The Institute offers a three-year undergraduate level programme which, in conjunction with an induction year teaching in school, leads towards QTS.

Length of course: 3 years f/t

Entry requirements: GCSE Maths, English and Science at grade C or above and three subjects at A-level or equivalent qualifications; interview.

Course content:
• Learning, teaching and the curriculum across the primary age range
• Primary curriculum subjects
• School experience
• Subject specialism: English

A separate pathway, Educational Studies, can be undertaken as part of an undergraduate Joint Honours course with other subjects in the Institute (eg Early Childhood Studies; Performing Arts; Sport and Coaching Studies; Theology, Communicaton, Media and Culture) or the wider university. However, this route does not lead directly to QTS.

Enquiries: Cliff Marshall; cmarshall@brookes.ac.uk; T: 01865 488359

CERTIFICATES / DIPLOMAS

■ PGCE Primary and Secondary Education

Length of course: 1 year f/t

Entry requirements: Applicants should have a degree and should normally have studied the subject in which they wish to specialise as a teacher for a substantial part of their time at university; they should have achieved a pass in both Maths and English at GCSE grade C or above and, for the Primary course, Science or the equivalent; interview.

Glossary on page XI

Course content:
- Learning, teaching and the curriculum across the appropriate age range
- Curriculum subjects
- School experience

Enquiries: Cliff Marshall; cmarshall@brookes.ac.uk; T: 01865 488359

■ **PGCE Post-Compulsory Education**
Length of course: 1 year f/t
Entry requirements: Applicants should have a degree and GCSE Maths, English and Science at grade C or above. Students without a degree but with professional and/or trade qualifications and work experience should apply for the *Certificate in Education (Post Compulsory Education)*, which is organised in the same way; interview.
Course content: The course begins with a 3-week introductory unit. Then, in early October, students start a three-day-a-week placement at a FE college, the other two days being spent at the Institute. By late November students will be teaching for nine hours a week at the college until late June.
Enquiries: Pat Hill; phill@brookes.ac.uk; T: 01865 488292

MASTER'S DEGREES

■ **MA in Education**
Length of course: 1 year f/t, normally 2-3 years p/t
Many of the pathways are also available through a combination of residential sessions and by distance learning to UK and overseas students.
Entry requirements: The programme is designed for experienced teachers and lecturers and managers in primary, secondary and post-compulsory education and for other professionals working in education.
Course content: The modular programme enables students to design their course according to their particular areas of interest. Students take nine modules to achieve the MA. Five of these are compulsory modules which are designed to support students' studies and to prepare them for the dissertation:
- Reflective Professional Development
- Educational Research
- Dissertation *(triple module)*

Four further modules are selected from the optional module programme. Depending on the choice made, the combination can lead to a named award, such as:
- MA in Education (International Schools)
- MA in Education Management
- MA in the Education of Able Pupils
- MA in Education (Multilingual Learning Contexts)
- MA in ICT and Learning
- MA in Special Educational Needs

The flexibility of the programme enables students to construct different pathways of study. This can lead to alternative post-graduate awards (Postgraduate Certificates and Diplomas in Educational Studies) which can be studied full-time or part-time. Some modules may also be taken individually as short courses.
Enquiries: Ashley Tagg; atagg@brookes.ac.uk; T: 01865 488284

- **MA in Educational Studies**

Length of course: 1 year f/t, 2 years p/t

Entry requirements: An honours degree in education or social sciences from a recognised university or an equivalent qualification; TOEFL at 600 or above or equivalent if English is not the applicant's first language.

Course content: Core modules:
- Comparative Studies in Education
- Developing Educational Research
- Dissertation *(triple module)*

Students then choose four optional modules which might include the following:
- Issues in Curriculum Design
- Child Development
- The Challenge of Bilingual and Multilingual Education
- Learning and Teaching
- Language and Learning in Education
- Educational Environments
- Information and Communication Technology in Teaching and Learning
- Research in Educational Management
- The Nature of Knowledge
- Ethics and Values in Education
- Developing Policy in Education

Enquiries: Louise Booker; lebooker@brookes.ac.uk; T: 01865 488555

RESEARCH DEGREES

The Institute of Education offers facilities for postgraduate students carrying out research on a full-time or part-time basis. It also hosts a number of visiting academics from overseas with experience and expertise in a wide range of research projects.

The Institute welcomes applications from anyone interested in conducting research towards MPhil, EdD and PhD degrees in a range of areas.

Faculty of Arts & Education
Douglas Avenue
EXMOUTH   EX8 2AT

T: 01395 255309
F: 01395 255303
E: fae-admissions@plymouth.ac.uk
W: www.plymouth.ac.uk

Dean: Professor Mike Newby

Rolle School of Education
Head of School: Mrs Gill Payne; T: 01395 255319

School of Graduate Studies in Arts & Education
Head of School: Dr Gordon Taylor; T: 01395 255316

Education provision in the Faculty is situated in the seaside town of Exmouth, Devon - eight miles from the historic city of Exeter. It is close to all transport services, motorway links and Exeter Airport and surrounded by some of the finest marine and natural landscapes in the UK.
The Rolle School of Education has considerable experience in the field of initial teacher education and is also increasingly involved in the study of early childhood.
The Graduate School has extensive provision of courses for professional educators both in schools and in the post-compulsory setor.

BACHELOR DEGREES

■ BEd Hons Primary
A flexible modular, CATS-rated course.
Length of course: 4 years
Entry requirements: GCSE Maths, English Language and Science at grade C or above and two subjects at A-level or equivalent qualifications.
Course content:
• Main subject studies from a choice of the following:
  • Art & Design
  • Early Childhood Studies
  • English
  • History
  • ICT
  • Music
  • Maths
  • PE
  • Science
• School experience
• Primary Core subject applications and methods of teaching
• Education studies
Fees: Non-EU students: £6300 for Early Childhood Studies, English, History, Maths
£7050 for other subjects

■ BA Hons Early Childhood Studies
A flexible modular course.
Length of course: 3 years f/t; equivalent p/t

Entry requirements: 2 subjects at A-level or equivalent qualifications.
Course content:
- Child Development
- Social Contexts of Childhood
- Comparative Provision for Children age 0-8

■ **BA Hons Steiner-Waldorf Education**
A flexible modular programme which prepares successful participants for teaching in Steiner-Waldorf Schools.
Length of course: 3 years f/t; p/t also possible
Course content:
- Anthroposophy
- Philosophy
- Subject Studies
- Comparative Studies
- Art
- Humanities & Sciences
- School Experience
Fees: Non-EU students: £6300

■ **BA Hons Education & Training**
Length of course: 2 years f/t; 3 years p/t
Entry requirements: Certificate in Education or equivalent; regular involvement in professional practice activities.
Course aims: To provide graduates with the opportunity to develop skills, knowledge and attitudes appropriate to their individual professional needs to become teachers, lecturers, trainers and adult education tutors in post-16 education, normally working outside the school system.
Course content: Core modules include:
- Teacher & Trainer Development
- Research Methods Theory in Education & Training
- Theory in Education & Training
- Management of Change Theory in Education & Training
- Psychology Theory in Education & Training
- Gender, Ethnicity & Education
- Comparative Education
- Current Developments in the Training Culture
Enquiries: Admissions; T: 01395 255478; F: 01395 255303; E: gsaeadmissions @plymouth.ac.uk

CERTIFICATES / DIPLOMAS / MASTER'S DEGREES

■ **PGCE Primary and Secondary**
Length of course: 1 year f/t
Entry requirements: A first degree or equivalent; GCSE at grade C or above or equivalent in Maths and English Language.
Course content: Secondary subjects:

- Art & Design
- Drama
- English
- Geography
- Maths
- Music

<u>Fees:</u> Non-EU students: £7050

■ PGCert/PGDip/MAEd - Integrated Master's Programme (Education)

<u>Length of course:</u> up to 5 years p/t, depending on which award participant is aiming for.

<u>Entry requirements:</u> A first degree or equivalent.

<u>Course aims:</u>
- To allow participants to select from a range of components to meet their particular requirements in terms of content, sequence and time.
- To enhance the quality of participants' practice through the encouragement of critical enquiry, innovative thinking and imaginative reformation.
- To ground participants' study in personal, professional and academic practice.

<u>Course structure/content:</u> This is a modular course of both taught and independent study modules. Modules include:
- Early Years Education
- Language & Literacy
- Post-16 Education
- Secondary Education
- Special Educational Needs

Two modules are awarded with the PGCert, four modules with the PHDip, four modules plus a dissertation with the MAEd.

<u>Assessment:</u> 4-5000-word assignments; dissertation for the MAEd.

<u>Enquiries:</u> Chris Lee, Programme Director; c.lee-2@plymouth.ac.uk; 01395 255465

■ CertEd/PGCE Post-Compulsory Education & Training

<u>Length of course:</u> 1 year f/t; 2 years p/t

<u>Entry requirements:</u> Normally for both awards, students must be actively engaged in a teacher/training capacity for 4-6 hours a week. For the PGCE, a first degree or equivalent is required.

<u>Course aims:</u>
- To provide graduates with the opportunity to develop skills, knowledge and attitudes appropriate to their individual professional needs to become teachers, lecturers, trainers and adult education tutors in post-16 education, normally working outside the school system.

<u>Course content:</u> Core modules include:
- Processes of Learning
- Processes of Teaching
- Developing & Understanding the Curriculum
- Research Methods

Portfolios:
- Contextualising Theory in Practice
- Professional Identity & Practice Style

• Curriculum & Resources
Enquiries: Admissions; T: 01395 255478; F: 01395 255303; E: gsaeadmissions
@plymouth.ac.uk

RESEARCH DEGREES

■ **MPhil/PhD**
Programmes of individual research and study, supervised by tutors with interests in a
wide variety of topics within the fields of Education, Humanities and Art & Design.
It is possible to transfer from the MPhil programme to the PhD programme.
Enquiries: Rosemary Hatch; r.hatch@plymouth.ac.uk; T: 01392 475087; F: 01392
2475012

OTHER COURSES

■ **Short Courses**
To suit individual needs of undergraduate students, shorter programmes can be
tailor-made from a wide range of modules offered in the Faculty of Arts and Education. The Credit Accumulation and Transfer Scheme enables credit to be awarded and
transferred to other institutions.

School of Education and Continuing Studies T: 023 9284 5222
St George's Building F: 023 9284 5200
141 High Street E: secs.shsc.enquiries@port.ac.uk
PORTSMOUTH PO1 2HY W: www.port.ac.uk/departments/secs

<u>Head of School:</u> Mike Coeshott

BACHELOR DEGREES

■ BA Hons Learning Support

This course is designed to meet the needs of those working in Learning Support settings within schools and other education and care establishments.

<u>Length of course:</u> 1-5 years p/t

<u>Entry requirements:</u> A range of qualifications are accepted, both in life-long learning experiences and formal qualifications. Prior learning will be taken into account.

<u>Course content:</u> The course aims to be flexible by offering various entry and exit points over five years and to suit the individual circumstances of the course member. As the course progresses, greater emphasis is put on independent study at Level 3 which is supervised and supported by tutors. The course is run in Portsmouth and the Isle of Wight, both with access to university facilities.

<u>Enquiries:</u> Irene Selway

■ BA Hons Education & Training

<u>Length of course:</u>

<u>Entry requirements:</u> Certificate in Education (Post-16/FE) or similar qualification.

<u>Course content:</u> This degree builds on and develops work completed in the Certificate in Education (Post-Compulsory Education and Further Education) and qualifications of similar nature for candidates who do not possess a degree. It provides an opportunity for those in training and education sectors to obtain an honours degree based on study that is directly relevant to their work and professional development.

CERTIFICATES / DIPLOMAS

■ PGCE Secondary

<u>Length of course:</u> 36 weeks f/t (September to July)

<u>Entry requirements:</u> A relevant recognised first degree; GCE/GCSE O-level English Language and Maths or equivalent; excellent command of English in order to fulfil the teaching practice requirements. All linguists will need French to O-level (or equivalent) standard.

<u>Course content:</u> Students specialise in teaching children aged 11-16. Subjects offered: English with Drama, Geography, Modern Languages, Maths, Secondary Science, Business Studies. The course provides professional preparation, including any subject knowledge appropriate to teaching which is not adequately covered by a relevant degree. The University and a large number of partner-schools jointly share responsibility for the student teacher's development and assessment of their competence. 120 days are spent on teaching practice with school time increasing as the course progresses. Students have the support of both school-based mentors and

university tutors whose aim is to help them develop confidence and competence and a high level of responsibility in the classroom.
Enquiries: Terry Ward

- **Certificate in Education/PGCE Post-compulsory Education**

This is a professional development course for lecturers, trainers, instructors and others who work in post-compulsory education.
Length of course: 1 year f/t; 2 years p/t
Entry requirements: *Certificate:* Interview; *PGCE:* Degree or equivalent
Course content: The course combines self-directed learning with a reflective practioner approach to enable course members to study while working in professional roles. It encompasses the eight Further Education National Training Organisation teaching standards and also supports the six National Key Skills at Levels 3 and 4. Taught sessions build on guided preparatory reading and active group participation.
Enquiries: Priscilla Rea
These courses are also available at the following FE Colleges:
Basingstoke College, Chichester College, Chippenham College, Eastleigh College, South Downs College.

MASTER'S DEGREES

- **MA Advanced Professional Practice in Education**

Length of course: 1 year f/t; 2-5 years p/t
Entry requirements: An honours degree or professional qualifications recognised as equivalent. Applicants must comply with University regulations for entry to Masters Degrees.
Course content: Units:
- Learning Agenda
- Evaluating Professional Practice
- Research Methods for Small-scale Applied Practice
- Mentoring in Professional Education
- Supporting Literacy in Schools
- Supporting Numeracy in Schools
- Special Needs in Edcuation
- Project Report
- Development Report
- *Any other unit with an education focus from the Faculty Modular Master's Scheme*
- Dissertation
Enquiries: Dr Angela Race

- **MSc Education & Training Management**

Length of course: 1 year f/t; 2-5 years p/t
Entry requirements: An honours degree or professional qualifications recognised as equivalent. Applicants must comply with University regulations for entry to Master's Degrees.
Course content: Units:

- Management of People in Organisations
- Principles of Marketing
- Management of Resource & Finance
- Management of Information Systems
- Management of the Curriculum
- Strategic Issues and the Management of Change
- Research Management and Methods: Individual Professional Development
- Individual & Professional Development
- Dissertation (12-15,000 words)

Assessment: Continuous within each taught unit.
Enquiries: Patricia Stallard

■ MA Health Professional Education

Length of course: 18 months p/t fast track; 2-5 years p/t
Entry requirements: An honours degree and professional qualifications. Applicants should comply with University regulations for entry to Master's Degrees.
Course content: Units in:
- Learning Agenda
- Teaching & Learning Theory & Practice
- Research Methods for Small-scale Applied Research
- Professional Development in Healthcare Education
- Assessing Practice in Nursing & Midwifery
- Mentorship in Health Professional Education
- Evaluating Professional Practice
- Development Report for Advanced Practice
- Projects Report
- *Any other health/education units from the Faculty Modular Master's Scheme*
- Dissertation

Enquiries: Dr Angela Race

■ Postgraduate Certificate/MA Learning & Teaching in Higher Education

Length of course: 3-5 years p/t
Entry requirements: Generally a first degree, but many students will have a higher degree and be involved in teaching in the HE sector.
Course content: The course aims to support HE teachers to enquire systematically and in-depth into chosen areas of professional academic practice related to learning and teaching. Course members will be expected to demonstrate current awareness of the range of issues and challenges facing the HE sector today and to provide coherent and constructive responses to such issues. They should also be able to contribute to the enhancement of the quality of learning and teaching within the institution in which they work.
The three core units which lead to the Postgraduate Certificate are accredited by the Institute of Learning and Teaching for their membership category.
Enquiries: Dorothy Haslehurst

RESEARCH DEGREES

■ MPhil, PhD

These are degrees for those wishing to undertake research into a significant educational topic. Programmes of research may be proposed in any field of educational theory and practice, subject to the requirement that the proposed programme is capable of leading to scholarly enquiry and its presentation for assessment. Research training is provided for all higher degree students.

<u>Length of course:</u> 18 (min) - 30 (max) months f/t
30 (min) - 48 (max) months p/t

<u>Entry requirements:</u> Normally an honours degree or a postgraduate diploma or professional qualification recognised as being equivalent to an honours degree. Other qualifications or experience which demonstrates that a candidate possesses appropriate knowledge; skills at honours degree standard may be acceptable.

<u>Assessment:</u> *MPhil:* Thesis not normally exceeding 40,000 words.

PhD: Thesis not normally exceeding 80,000 words.

<u>Enquiries:</u> Dr David Holloway

Faculty of Education and Community Studies

Bulmershe Court

Earley

READING   RG6 1HY

T: 0118 931 8810
F: 0118 935 2080
E: edug@reading.ac.uk
W: www.rdg.ac.uk

Dean of Faculty: Professor David Malvern

BACHELOR DEGREES

■ BA(Ed) Hons

This course is for Early Years (age 3-8) or Late Primary (age 7-12) teachers.

Length of course: 4 years f/t

Entry requirements: English Language, Maths and Science at GCSE grade C or above and two A-levels at grades B, C or equivalent; interview.

Course content: Subject Specialism Courses on offer are: Art, English, Music.

Fees: EU students: £1075
      Non-EU students: £7779

Enquiries: Dr Les James (contact details see above)

CERTIFICATES / DIPLOMAS

■ PGCE Primary

University-based and school-based professional course for those wishing to teach children in the age ranges 3-7 or 7-11.

Length of course: 12 months f/t (38 weeks)

Entry requirements: Degree relevant to Primary Teaching plus GCSE grade C or above in Maths, English Language and Science or equivalents. Ability to communicate effectively in spoken English and to study through the medium of English.

Course content: Students are prepared to teach across the curriculum and in a variety of school settings including inner-city and multi-racial schools.

Assessment: Coursework, including practical teaching.

Fees: EU students: £1075
      Non-EU students: £7779

Enquiries: Mr Paul Wells (contact details see above)

■ PGCE Secondary

Length of course: 12 months f/t (36 weeks)

Entry requirements: Degree relevant to the proposed teaching subject plus GCSE grade C or above in Maths and English Language or equivalents.

Course content: University-based and school-based professional course on the teaching and assessment of a school subject chosen from the following: Art, Biology, Chemistry, Drama, English, French, Geography, German, History, Italian and French, Maths, Music, PE. University-based and school-based work on Complementary Studies (general principles, whole school issues, cross-circular elements, role of the form tutor).

Assessment: Coursework, including practical teaching.

Fees: EU students: £1075
      Non-EU students: £7779

Enquiries: Dr Martin Parsons (contact details see beginning of entry)

UNIVERSITY OF READING

- **PGCE Secondary Modern Languages: French (Conversion course)**
Length of course: 2 years f/t (72 weeks)
Entry requirements: A good class degree in any subject; advanced level French.
Course structure/content: The first year of this course provides intensive tuition in French (including six weeks in France) to achieve degree standard. This leads to entry to the 1-year PGCE Secondary MFL, which comprises three main parts: Language; Culture; Introduction to the Classroom. In addition to the PGCE Qualified Teacher Status, students are awarded a Post-experience Diploma in French for the secondary classroom.
Assessment: Course work and end of year examination.
Fees: EU students: £1075
      Non-EU students: £7779
Enquiries: Postgraduate Admissions Office, Faculty of Education & Community Studies; edug@reading.ac.uk; 0118 931 8816

CERTIFICATES / DIPLOMAS / MASTER'S DEGREES

- **PGDip/MA in English & Language in Education**
Length of course: 12 months f/t; 2-4 years p/t
Entry requirements: Degree or other suitable qualification; normally two years' relevant experience.
Course content: This modular course explores educational aspects of Language, Literature, Drama, English Teaching, Reading, Writing, Gender, IT, Media Education.
Assessment: *Diploma:* coursework
      MA: 15-20,000-word dissertation
Fees: EU students: £2805
      Non-EU students: £6900
Enquiries: Mr Andrew Goodwyn *(contact details see beginning of entry)*

- **PGDip/MA in IT in Education**
Length of course: 12 months f/t; 2-3 years p/t (one afternoon and evening per week)
Entry requirements: Degree or equivalent; PGCE; at least two years' teaching experience.
Course content: The course is designed to provide students with the skills and understanding necessary to develop and coordinate IT across the curriculum and includes both practical and educational studies.
Assessment: *Diploma:* mixture of practical assignments, essays and examinations
      MA: 15-20,000-word dissertation
Fees: EU students: £2805
      Non-EU students: £6900
Enquiries: Dr Patrick Carmichael *(contact details see beginning of entry)*

- **PGDip/MA in Music Education**
Length of course: 12 months f/t; 2-4 years p/t
Entry requirements: Degree in Music or equivalent; normally not less than two years' teaching experience.
Course content: Modules include:

- Theories of Music Curriculum Content & Structure
- Current Issues
- Music Microtechnology
- Creativity & Classroom Composition
- Personality, Music & Educational Processes
- Historical Aspects
- Music & Society
- The Voice in Education

Assessment: *Diploma:* coursework

　　　　　　MA:　　15-20,000-word dissertation

Fees: EU students:　　£2805

　　　Non-EU students: £6900

Enquiries: Dr Gordon Cox *(contact details see beginning of entry)*

■ **PGDip/MA in Organisation, Planning & Management in Education**

Length of course: 12 months f/t; 2 years p/t

Entry requirements: Degree, PGCE; at least two years teaching experience.

Course content: The course is designed to introduce students to management problems, financial issues, changing educational patterns and contemporary educational policy issues from a comparative and international perspective. There is a strong emphasis on education in developing countries, adult & continuing education and literacy, combined with perspectives from Social Sciences. The course has specialist recognition from the ESRC.

Assessment: By coursework and dissertation. The dissertation provides an opportunity for sustained study of an issue or topic of the student's own choice.

Fees: EU students:　　£2740

　　　Non-EU students: £6657

Enquiries: Dr Kevin Brehony *(contact details see beginning of entry)*

■ **PGDip/MA in Inclusive Education**

Length of course: 12 months f/t; 2-4 years p/t

Entry requirements: Degree or equivalent; normally two years' teaching experience.

Course content: The course introduces students to the latest thinking about the inclusion of pupils with disabilities and difficulties in learning in mainstream education. The core modules are:

- School Development & Provision for Difficulties in Learning
- Enhancing Pupil Learning
- SEN - Policies & Practice

Assessment: *Diploma:* coursework

　　　　　　MA:　　15-20,000-word dissertation

Fees: EU students:　　£2805

　　　Non-EU students: £6900

Enquiries: Dr Ghazala Bhatti *(contact details see beginning of entry)*

MASTER'S DEGREES

■ MA (Research) in Education & Community Studies

Length of course: 12 months f/t; 2-3 years p/t

Entry requirements: Degree

Course content:
- Research Methods Course: Introduction to Social Research
- Design & Conduct of Social Research
- Qualitative Research Methods of Data Collection & Analysis
- Quantitative Research Methods of Data Collection & Analysis
- Producing a Thesis
- Practical Philosophies of Social Research
- Preparation of 30-40,000-word thesis

Areas of research represented in the Faculty are listed in the MPhil/PhD section below.

Assessment: Coursework for Research Methods course; a 30-40,000-word thesis.

Fees: EU students: £2805
      Non-EU students: £6900

Enquiries: Dr Ghazala Bhatti *(contact details see beginning of entry)*

RESEARCH DEGREES

■ MPhil, PhD

Entry requirements: Degree or equivalent in appropriate subject and relevant practical experience.

Research areas: Education in:
- Art & Design
- English
- Environment
- French
- Geography & Earth Sciences
- German
- History
- IT
- Language & Literacy
- Maths
- Music
- Science (all branches)
- Technology

Teaching and Learning at: primary, secondary, further, adult, higher, professional, continuing levels.

Perspectives on Education from: History, Psychology, Sociology, Philosophy.

Themes: comparative, Development, Special Needs, Safety, multicultural (especially linguistic), Education, Community Health, Counselling, Vocational Guidance, Youth Work.

Assessment: Coursework within Research Methods Course; thesis submission; viva voce.

Fees: EU students: £2805
      Non-EU students: £6900

Enquiries: Dr Pam Denicolo *(contact details see beginning of entry)*

Faculty of Education
Froebel College
Roehampton Lane
LONDON SW15 5PJ

T: 020 8392 3232
F: 020 8392 3470
E: enquiries@roehampton.ac.uk
W: www.roehampton.ac.uk

Enquiries: Enquiries Office, University of Surrey Roehampton, Whitelands College, West Hill, London SW15 3SN
(for Research Degrees and 'Other Courses' see under appropriate entry below)

The Roehampton Institute London was created in 1975 with the federation of four colleges: Froebel College, Digby Stuart, Southlands and Whitelands, each of which fully contributes to the academic pursuit of excellence, professional preparation and vocational tuition that characterises the Institute. In January 2000, the Institute entered federation with the University of Surrey and achieved university status as *University of Surrey Roehampton*. Roehampton is a thriving, innovative learning environment and has over 6000 students, nearly 5000 of whom are undergraduates. The University benefits from being both conveniently close to the West End of London and open parkland. All awards are made by the University of Surrey.

BACHELOR DEGREES

■ BA Hons Primary Education
Teaching Studies is one of the justly renowned specialisms of University of Surrey Roehampton. Students benefit from the resources of one of Britain's largest primary teacher education centres, acclaimed for its pioneering work.
Length of course: 3 years f/t
Entry requirements: 14 A-level points or equivalent; GCSE passes at grade C in English Language and Maths (and Science for applicants born on or after 1 Sept. 1979) or acceptable equivalents; applicants must meet the entry requirements for their chosen subject specialism.
Course content: The programme is designed to reflect the needs of the primary teacher and the nature of the primary curriculum in the 21st century. The course allows time to develop subject knowledge, teaching skills and experience, gain a thorough understanding of children and the curriculum, to reflect on these experiences and build the competence and confidence essential to a primary teacher.
Assessment: Coursework in the form of essays, reports, presentations, assignments and projects; assessment of practical competence; certain subject specialisms may include some written examinations.

■ BA/BSc Education
Length of course: 3 years f/t; up to 7 years p/t
Entry requirements: 12 A-level points; NVQ and GNVQ Advanced are accepted.
Course content: This degree takes people and their education as its central topic. It is firmly based in the humanities, making use of philosophy, history, psychology and sociology, with strong contributions from both sciences and the arts. It is a lively, controversial subject and teaching structures reflect this, allowing plenty of time for discussion. The programme forms part of a Combined Honours degree programme.
Assessment: Revealed written papers or assignments, or extended reports.

■ **BA Early Childhood Studies**
Length of course: 3 years f/t; up to 7 years p/t
Entry requirements: 12 A-level points; GNVQ Advanced and BTEC National Diploma
also accepted. Alternative qualifications considered on individual basis.
Course content: The programme focuses on the strands of knowledge which underlie
all professional work with young children. It considers the diversity of services provided for families with young children and offers the opportunity to gain in-depth
understanding of the nature of childhood and of the role of the adult in working with
children. The programme may be studied on its own or in combination with another
programme at Honours level.
Assessment: A variety of assessment modes are used including essays, presentations
and position papers.

CERTIFICATES / DIPLOMAS

■ **Modular Programmes**
Individual courses, with or without assessment are available in: Arts Management,
Counselling in Education, D&T, Drugs Education, Early Childhood, ICT, Return to
Teaching (Primary or Secondary), Science Education, SEN
Credits gained on successful completion of individual courses count towards a wide
range of Certificates and Diplomas. A Foundation Certificate for classroom assistants
is also available.
Length of course: Variable, 1 term minimum
Entry requirements: Normally at least two years of HE experience or equivalent; addi-
tional qualifications may be required for a particular named award.
Assessment: Each course is examined at specified times by assignments in a form
prescribed by the course tutor.

■ **PGCE Primary and Secondary**
Length of course: 1 year f/t
Entry requirements: A degree awarded by an approved university or acceptable equiva-
lent (for secondary PGCE, initial qualifications should be in the subject specialism or
an allied area); GCSE/O level passes at minimum grade C in Maths and English Lan-
guage; some recent relevant work in primary or secondary schools.
Course content:
Primary: Students elect to specialise in either Early Years and K/S 1 (3-8 years) or K/S 2
(7-11 years).
Secondary: prepares graduates with appropriate degrees to teach in one of ten areas:
Art, Business Studies, D&T, English, History, Maths, Modern Languages, Music, RE,
Science.
Assessment: Assignment and assessment of practical competence.

MASTER'S DEGREES

■ **MA Early Childhood Studies**
■ **MA Art, Craft & Design Education**
■ **MA Choral Education**

■ MA Education

Length of courses: 1 year f/t; up to 4 years p/t

Entry requirements: First degree (in education or one in which education is a significant component) or a first degree plus PGCE or Certificate in Education recognised by the DfEE for QTS or a comparable professional award plus relevant experiential learning.

Course content: The MA Education Programme offers opportunities, subject to viability, for specialisation in: Careers Guidance, D&T, Education Management, ICT, Language & Literacy, Leadership in Anglican or Catholic Schools, Maths Education, RE, Science Education, SEN, Teaching & Learning in HE.

All programmes include courses on Research Methods and Enquiry and a dissertation and focus on the improvement of professional knowledge and practice through critical self-reflection and the study of relevant theory and recent research. Graduate Certificates and Graduate Diplomas can also be taken in any of the above areas.

Assessment: Assignments, files or diaries, case studies, research reports, practical projects, seminar papers or presentations; dissertation.

RESEARCH DEGREES

■ MPhil, PhD

The Faculty of Education supports a wide range of research activities through well-established Teaching Studies Areas. The involvement of the Faculty in all major teacher education initiatives ensures that links with the local community of schools and related agencies are extensive and well-supported. There is a strong international representation among our substantial group of full-time research students. At present we have students from South Korea, Malaysia, Canada, Portugal, Brazil, Greece, Qatar and Italy. Part-time graduate students are also well represented and many of these combine research with their professional teaching commitments.

Entry requirements: First or second class honours degree in Education or with Education as a significant component.

Assessment: Thesis and Viva Voce.

Enquiries: Enquiries Office, RIDO, University of Surrey Roehampton, Roehampton Lane, London SW15 5PH; T: 020 8392 3628

OTHER COURSES

■ Short Courses
■ Consultancy

We offer a wide range of short courses which can be tailored to suit specific needs. Consultancy can be negotiated to cover a wide range of educational topics. Both types of services can offered abroad by arrangement. An Attendance Certificate is issued to all course participants and accreditation can be arranged.

Enquiries: Pauline Lewis, CPD Office, T: 020 8392 3383; F: 020 8392 3664; *(address see 'Enquiries' at beginning of entry)*

Department of Educational Studies   T: 0114 222 8087
School of Education   F: 0114 279 6236
388 Glossop Road   E: education@sheffield.ac.uk
SHEFFIELD S10 2JA   W: www.shef.ac.uk/education
Enquiries: Lorraine Roe; l.roe@sheffield.ac.uk

CERTIFICATES / DIPLOMAS

Students whose qualifications do not meet the requirements for entry to the Masters degrees below have the opportunity to follow the programmes at Diploma level. For further details contact the Department.

MASTER'S DEGREES

■ MA in Early Childhood Education

Length of course: 2 years p/t
Entry requirements: A first degree or Diploma in Advanced Studies in Education; a minimum of 3 years of teaching experience or other appropriate work.
Course content: Students study the following modules:
- Early Childhood Education: History and Policy
- Development Learning & Curriculum
- Contemporary Issues in Early Childhood Education
- Research Methods in Early Childhood Education
A 60-credit dissertation is also taken.
Fees: *on application*

■ MEd in Educational Studies

Length of course: 12 months and 1 week
Entry requirements: A first degree or a Diploma in Advanced Studies in Education; two years' teaching or appropriate Educational work. Students for whom English is not their first language must also meet the University requirement of 6.0 on the IELTS or 550 (paper-based)/213 (computer-based) on the TEOFL scales for English as a foreign language (proof of this standard is required).
Course content: Students study four modules which are interrelated to ensure continuity and to encourage students to engage in the research and methodological issues which they are interested in exploring. One module (Culture, Difference & Diversity: Current Issues) is specifically designed to explore issues relating to students' own institutional, cultural and social contexts, which can then be developed further in their independent study. Students can negotiate with the Course Director to specialise in a number of areas which relate to the Department's Research Centres (Curriculum & Pedagogy; Inclusive Education; Post-Compulsory Education & Training; Literacy; Education, Change, Innovation & Policy; Higher Education). An important element of the course is the attachment of students to the Department's Research. The taught programme is timetabled on two days per week. From May to September students work towards completing a dissertation of 20-25,000 words. In addition to the taught course, there is a structured programme of support for students which includes assignment writing, using the library and dissertation workshops. Students are supported throughout their study with a personal tutor and a dissertation supervisor. A

social programme of activities is planned with events throughout the year so that students can experience some of the social and cultural activities which Yorkshire has to offer. In addition to the support provided within the Department, there are University support agencies available to students.

Assessment: A 6000-word assignment for each module; 20-25,000-word dissertation (no formal written examinations).

Fees: *on application*

■ **MEd in English Language Teaching** (distance learning)

Length of course: 2 years p/t

Entry requirements: A first degree or Diploma in Advanced Studies in Education; a minimum of two years' teaching experience or other appropriate educational work.

Course content: The course has a 30-credit Foundation Module which is based on the rationale that teachers need an understanding of learning, the curriculum and teaching to inform their practice. Students then take the following three modules:

• Language
• Issues & Processes in Language Learning & Teaching
• Management of ELT *or* The Adult Learner

Assessment: Four 6000-word assignments and a 20,000-word dissertation

Fees: *on application*

■ **MEd in Literacy Education** (distance learning)

Length of course: 2 years p/t

Entry requirements: *see MEd in English Language Teaching above*

Applications are welcome from those working in pre-school, primary, secondary and adult settings.

Course content: Students study the following modules:

• The Development of Literacy
• The Literacy Curriculum
• Literacy in a Wider Context
• Methods of Literacy Research

Assessment: A 6000-word assignment for each module; a 60-credit dissertation.

Fees: *on application*

■ **MEd in Educational Management** (distance learning)

Length of course: 2 years p/t

Entry requirements: *see MEd in English Language Teaching above*

Course content: Students study the following modules:

• The Foundation Module
• Managing Educational Institutions
• Managing People in Schools & Colleges
• Principles & Practices of Managing Change in Education

Assessment: Four 6000-word assignments and a 20,000-word dissertation

Fees: *on application*

■ **MEd in Inclusive Education** (distance learning)

Length of course: 2 years p/t

Entry requirements: *see MEd in English Language Teaching above*

The course is designed to be flexible and applications are welcomed from those working in pre-school settings, primary and secondary schools, FE and HE.
Course content: Students study the following 30-credit modules:
• Insider Perspectives
• Difference & Difficulty
• Learning, Management & Curriculum
• Cross-Cultural Issues in Special & Inclusive Education
Assessment: Four 6000-word assignments and a 60-credit dissertation (20,000 words)
Fees: on application

■ **MEd in Science Education** (distance learning)
   Available only from the Cyprus base.
Length of course: 2 years p/t
Entry requirements: *see MEd in English Language Teaching above*
Course content: Students study the following modules:
• The Foundation Module
• Learning, Teaching & Assessment in Science Education
• Issues & Developments in Science Education
• Research Methods in Science Education
Assessment: A 6000-word assignment for each module; a 60-credit dissertation.
Fees: on application

■ **MEd in E-Learning**
Length of course: 2 years p/t
Entry requirements: A first degree or equivalent professional experience.
Course content: Students participate in 3 workshops:
• An Introduction to on-line learning communities
• Networked learning and computer supported co-operative learning
• The Internet as a learning environment
This is followed up by planning and designing an action research project and a research dissertation.
Fees: on application

RESEARCH DEGREES

■ **MPhil, PhD**
Length of course: *MPhil:* 1 year; *PhD:* 3 years (min)
Entry requirements: A good honours or postgraduate degree from an approved University or equivalent qualification.
Course content: Supervision is available in many areas of education and a list of staff research interests will be sent on request.   A student's supervisor will organise a programme of work and there is a Graduate School research training programme in place. Students registered for MPhil may be permitted to transfer to PhD after presentation of a 10,000 word defence paper and viva.
Assessment: Thesis (written in English) and oral examination.
Fees: £7050

■ **EdD**

Length of course: 4 years p/t (min)

Entry requirements: A good honours or postgraduate degree from an approved University or equivalent qualification.

Course content: This is a structured programme based around residential weekends that incorporates six research modules with a thesis that involves sustained research on a particular issue or topic. The course is designed to provide a broad and flexible research-based programme that will be relevant to a range of professional and managerial careers.

Fees: £1840

OTHER COURSES

■ **Overseas Learning Centres**

Some of the above courses are also available at our Overseas Learning Centres in Singapore, Cyprus and the Caribbean.

School of Education
36 Collegiate Crescent
Collegiate Crescent Campus
SHEFFIELD S10 2BP

T: 0114 225 2306
F: 0114 225 2324
E: education@shu.ac.uk
W: www.shu.ac.uk/schools/ed

The School of Education, which has one of the largest teacher education programmes in the United Kingdom, offers to overseas colleagues a wide range of development opportunities. Basic information is provided below; for more detail and the most up-to-date information, please contact us (see details above) or see our website.

MASTER'S DEGREES

The School of Education runs a comprehensive range of courses for practitioners professionally engaged in education and training, including
- Educational Inclusion
- Post-Compulsory Education & Training
- Leadership & Management
- Curriculum Studies
- Counselling
- Autism
- Multimedia

For a comprehensive list of courses currently available, please see our website.
Length of courses: normally 1 year f/t
Entry requirements: normally a first degree and relevant experience.

RESEARCH DEGREES

■ MPhil, PhD, EdD (taught)
Length of course: PhD: normally 3 years f/t (min)
                   MPhil: normally 2 years f/t (min)
                   EdD: normally 4 years p/t
Entry requirements: A good honours or postgraduate degree from an approved university (or an equivalent qualification).

OTHER COURSES

■ Group Study Programmes
The School has much experience in designing and delivering tailor-made study programmes for groups. For details contact Customer Services *(contact details above)*.

■ Visiting Fellowships and Visiting Professorships
The School welcomes education professionals who wish to use it as a base for research and other scholarly activities and to make a contribution to the academic life of the University.

Division of Education
103 Borough Road
LONDON SE1 0AA

T: 020 7815 8125
F: 020 7815 8160
E: inmansj@sbu.ac.uk
W: www.sbu.ac.uk/fhss/education/

Head of Division of Education: Sally Inman

The Faculty of Humanities and Social Science offers a range of courses at both under-graduate and postgraduate level and professional development courses for teachers, lecturers and administrators throughout the education service.

CERTIFICATES / DIPLOMAS

■ PGCE Primary
Length of course: 1 academic year (38 weeks) f/t
Entry requirements: A good honours degree in a National Curriculum subject or a good honours degree plus A-level at grade C or above in National Curriculum sub-jects; GCSEs at grade C or above in English and Maths; Science at grade C or above if born after 1979; school experience.
Course content: The course aims to initiate graduates into the professional role of the teacher, including becoming conversant with the Education Reform Act, the National Literacy and Numeracy strategies and subsequent legislation, developing all round professional competence.
Applications: through GTTR (see Glossary)
Enquiries: Pauline Watts; wattspa@sbu.ac.uk; T: 020 7815 8071

■ Modular PGCE Primary
The PGCE course above is also available in a modular mode, enabling people who wish to become teachers but cannot undertake a full-time programme of study, to gain QTS. The programme resembles that of the PGCE and the GTP (see below).
Length of course: 2 years max (length will vary according to entry qualifications)
Entry requirements: see PGCE above

■ Graduate and Registered Teacher Programmes
SBU offers three TTA-approved programmes which cover Primary Education (3-11):
1. The Graduate Teacher Programme
QTS is awarded upon successful completion.
Length of course: 1 year
Entry requirements: Degree; GCSE Maths and English; aged 24 or over. Overseas qualifications must be compatible with UK qualifications and checked by NARIC*.
Course content: Trainees follow a one day a week academic course and work four days a week as a supernumerary teacher.
2. The Registered Teacher Programme
A BA in Education with QTS is awarded upon successful completion.
Length of course: 2 years
Entry requirements: Two years Higher Education; GCSE Maths and English; aged 24 or over. Overseas qualifications must be compatible with UK qualifications and checked by NARIC*.

Course content: Trainees follow a one day a week academic course and work four days a week in schools.

3. Overseas Trained Teacher Programme

Overseas Trained Teachers with teaching experience in the UK can apply for a final assessment only. Once QTS has been awarded and the OTT has taught in the UK for two years s/he can apply to be assessed against the NQT standards.

A short training programme can be arranged for OTTs if they require training before the final assessment.

If the candidate elects SBU to be the Recommending Body, SBU will undertake the final assessment.

Entry requirements: Degree; GCSE Maths and English; aged 24 or over. Overseas qualifications must be compatible with UK qualifications and checked by NARIC*.

Note: All trainees must pass the TTA skills tests before they can be awarded QTS.

* www.naric.org.uk; T: 01242 260010

MASTER'S DEGREES

■ MA Programme in Education

This programme is aimed at teachers in primary and secondary schools, FE colleges and HE institutions.

Length of course: Variable; the programme can be studied through part-time evening attendance or distance learning.

Entry requirements: Normally practicing teachers or educators with a good honours degree or equivalent; at least three years' teaching experience. Careful consideration will be given to candidates who do not meet the standard entry requirements, bearing in mind that the course aims to attract good practitioners with the motivation, confidence and potential to study at this level.

Course content: The course provides students with a theoretical perspective drawing on, while extending and deepening, their professional experience and expertise. The programme is flexible and students may, if they wish, seek to register for single units only. Successful completion of these units can be counted towards an award (SBU Certificate, SBU Diploma, PGDip, MA, MSc) if the student subsequently decides to work towards one of these.

Assessment: By coursework and dissertation.

Fees: £130 per unit; £410 dissertation (EU students)

Enquiries: Peter Winbourne; peter.winbourne@sbu.ac.uk; T: 020 7815 7452

RESEARCH DEGREES

■ MPhil, PhD

Research areas:
• Computing Education
• Early Years Education
• History & History Education
• Internet & Education
• Language & Literacy

- Language Needs of Teachers
- Maths Education
- Professionalism of Teachers

Enquiries: Prof Stephen Lerman; lermans@sbu.ac.uk; T: 020 7815 7440
Fees: Contact Bev Goring; goringbl@sbu.ac.uk; T: 020 7815 5796

OTHER COURSES

■ **Short Courses**
A range of short courses is offered, notably in the main curriculum areas and in professional development. Tailor-made courses are available by arrangement, including courses in pre-inspection, APL and school management and planning. Fees are charged according to the length and nature of the course.
Enquiries: Sally Inman; inmansj@sbu.ac.uk

UNIVERSITY OF SOUTHAMPTON

Research and Graduate School of Education
SOUTHAMPTON   SO17 1BJ

T: 023 8059 3475
F: 023 8059 3556
E: rgseaco@soton.ac.uk
W: www.education.soton.ac.uk

Head of School: Professor Nick Foskett
Enquiries: 023 8059 2413 (PGCE admissions); 023 8059 3476 (Masters/Research)

The Research and Graduate School of Education has a particular interest in fostering international co-operation in education. Several staff members have considerable experience both in comparative studies and of work in developing countries.

CERTIFICATES / DIPLOMAS

■ Diploma / Certificate in Advanced Educational Studies
Courses are available on a part-time basis in a wide range of subjects.
Entry requirements: A first degree; 2 years relevant experience.
Fees: *EU students: £645; Non-EU students: £2890*

■ PGCE Primary and Secondary
Length of courses: 1 years f/t
Entry requirements: A first degree.
Course content: The Primary course is concerned with teaching children up to 11 years old, the secondary course with 11-18 year olds. Both courses include a substantial amount of teaching practice.
Applications: via the GTTR *(see Glossary)*
Fees: *EU students: £1100; Non-EU students: £7520*

MASTER'S DEGREES

■ MA in Applied Linguistics for Language Teaching
Length of course: 1 year f/t
Entry requirements: Normally a good first degree of an approved university; at least 2 years' relevant professional experience.
Course content: This course provides post-experience professional development for language educators with interests in both language and literature. It is especially suitable for overseas teachers, advisers, etc, with interests in the teaching of English as a second/foreign language.

■ MA in English Language Teaching
Length of course: 1 year f/t
Entry requirements: Normally a first degree in a relevant subject; substantial professional experience of ELT (at least 2 years). International students must meet the standard English language requirements of the University.
Course content: The MA ELT is a post-experience programme which provides teachers of English as a foreign language with the opportunity to:
• reflect on their professional experience
• develop a deeper understanding of the theory and practice of ELT
• gain the skills and competences required for leadership roles in ELT

Glossary on page XI

■ **MA Education**

MA(Ed) degrees are offered in the following areas:
• Geographical and/or Environmental Education
• Institutional & Professional Development
• Language in Education (including the opportunity to specialise in Linguistics, TOEFL, Literature and Media Studies)
• Management & Professional Studies in Education
• Maths Education
• Physical Education & Curriculm Change
• Science & Technology Education

Length of course: 1 year f/t (with a dissertation to be submitted by 23 September following the period of instruction)

Entry requirements: Normally a first degree of an approved university or recognised teaching qualification; at least 3 years' professional experience in education or in a closely related field.

Course content: These courses are suitable for teachers, lecturers, advisers, administrators, adult educators, education officers, educational researchers and others engaged in educational and closely linked activities. Participants are given opportunities to specialise in areas which interest them and students from overseas are encouraged to deal with topics relevant to their countries.

Assessment: By course work and dissertation.

■ **MSc Education**

The MSc(Ed) course is organised similarly to the MA(Ed) course, but combines studies in education with one of the following:
• Environmental Science
• Geography
• Science & Technology
• Specific Learning Difficulties/Dyslexia

Length of course: 1 year f/t

Entry requirements: Normally a first degree or equivalent; 3 years' professional experience.

■ **MSc Health Education / Health Promotion**

Length of course: 1 year f/t

Entry requirements: First degree and relevant experience.

Course content:
• Principles of Health Education / Health Promotion
• Health Education / Health Promotion in Action
• Development and Change in Health Education / Health Promotion
• Assessed work

■ **MSc Computer-Based Learning / Training**

Length of course: 1 year f/t

Entry requirements: First degree and relevant experience.

Course content:
• Foundations of IT
• Principles of Computer-based Learning/Training
• Software and Courseware Design & Evaluation

Glossary on page XI

- Multimedia Technologies for Learning & Training
- Authoring the Learning & Training Process

Fees: (all MA / MSc courses) *EU students: £2890; Non-EU students: £7520*

RESEARCH DEGREES

■ MPhil, PhD
Length of course: *MPhil:* 12 months (min) f/t; *PhD:* 24 months (min) f/t
Entry requirements: Normally a first degree of an approved university or equivalent qualification; at least 3 years of professional experience in education or in a closely related field. Applicants are required to submit a specific proposal.
Course content: The School is able to provide supervision for research on a wide range of topics. Full-time students follow a broad training programme in research methods in Year 1. An MPhil or PhD may also be awarded for work related to an appropriate development project.
The School encourages overseas students to undertake research related to the needs of their country. Special arrangements can be made for combining full-time and part-time registration, to allow for periods of research in the student's own country.
Assessment: By thesis.

■ MPhil Research Methodology
This course is the taught degree equivalent of the MPhil by research as noted above.
Length of course: 1 year f/t
Entry requirements: Master's degree or equivalent.
Course content:
- Philosophical Context of Research
- Strategies in Educational Research
- Methods & Data in Educational Research
- Research Processes & Skills
- Options
- Assessed work

Assessment: Coursework (30,000 words); dissertation (20,000 words).

■ EdD
Length of course: 3 years (min) f/t
Entry requirements: Normally a Masters degree of an approved university in an appro-priate specialism; professional experience in a relevant area.
Course content: The EdD programme is offered in each of five main fields:
- Management in Education
- Evaluation & Change
- Auto/Biographical Studies
- Educational Psychology
- Health Education

The EdD includes a substantial taught element. The doctorate is designed to meet the needs of those involved in education, training, social and caring professions who are seeking to extend and deepen their knowledge and understanding of contemporary education issues.
Assessment: By a combination of assignments, a research thesis and an oral examination.
Fees: *EU students: £3700; Non-EU students: £7520*

Academic Registry
Stranmillis Road
BELFAST   BT9 5DY

T: 028 9038 1271
F: 028 9066 4423
E: registry@stran.ac.uk
W: www.stran.ac.uk

Enquiries: Mae Watson, Director External Affairs; m.watson@stran.ac.uk; T: 028 9038 1271

Stranmillis University College is located in South Belfast. Its students enjoy a purpose-built campus in a conservation area, occupying an enclosed site of 46 acres of woodland rich in wildlife. It is within walking distance of shops, restaurants, clubs and theatres. The University College is academically integrated with Queen's University Belfast. It was founded in 1922 to provide state-funded teacher education in Northern Ireland and has a track record of which it can be extremely proud. Within the past academic year, education provision at Stranmillis gained the highest possible marks - 24 in each category - for quality by the Quality Assurance Agency. The QAA is the body charged by Government with the task of monitoring the quality of all higher education provision in the UK.

Major research strengths in Stranmillis University College are in the fields of:
- Social Inclusion, including special educational needs, values education and citizenship
- Teacher Education, including initial land continuing professional development and higher education teaching
- Early Childhood Education, including the pre-school curriculum

The specific welfare and social needs of overseas students are provided for through a range of agencies and personnel such as the Director of Student Affairs and Advisers of Studies. Students can be accommodated in Halls of Residence, some of which are self-catering, on the Campus. The University College campus also provides dining and recreational facilities. Students at Stranmillis enjoy a double advantage: On the one hand, they are part of a small, caring community on a Campus of less than one thousand full-time students; on the other hand, as students of Queen's University, they also benefit from all the facilities offered by a large university with an international reputation.

BACHELOR DEGREES

■ BEd Primary/Secondary Education
Length of course: 4 years f/t
Entry requirements: GCE A-levels or equivalent qualification; GCSE or equivalent in English, Maths; also Science for Primary Education.
Course content: Students complete 24 modules in Education and Professional Studies, Curriculum Studies and spend eight weeks in schools undertaking school-based work.
Assessment: Continuous assessment and formal examination.
Fees: £6115 pa

- **BA Early Childhood Studies**

Length of course: 3 years f/t; 4 years p/t

Entry requirements: GCE A-levels or equivalent qualification; GCSE or equivalent in English, Maths, Science.

Course content: Students complete 18 modules relating to psychological and sociological approaches to the study of young children; work placement and personal development portfolio.

Assessment: Continuous assessment and formal examination.

Fees: £6115 pa

- **BSc Health & Leisure Studies**

Length of course: 3 years f/t

Entry requirements: GCE A-levels or equivalent qualification; GCSE or equivalent in English, Maths, Science.

Course content: Students complete 18 modules relating to health, leisure and sport; work.

Assessment: Continuous assessment and formal examination.

Fees: £6115 pa

CERTIFICATES / DIPLOMAS

- **PGCE Primary**

Length of course: 1 year f/t

Entry requirements: An honours degree of an approved university; relevant experience.

Course content: Educational Studies; Curriculum; School and Community; Classroom Management; Pastoral Issues; school-based work.

Assessment: Continuous assessment.

Fees: £7315

School of Education
Hammerton Hall
Gray Road
SUNDERLAND   SR2 8JB

T: 0191 515 2395
F: 0191 515 2629
W: www.sund.ac.uk

<u>Director of School:</u> Professor George Shield

BACHELOR DEGREES

- **BA Hons in**
  Early Years Education (4 years)
  Junior Years Education (4 years)
  Key Stage 2/3 IT Education (3 years)
  Early Childhood Studies (non-QTS)

- **BA Hons Secondary in**
  Business Education (2 years f/t)
  Design & Technology Education (2 years f/t)
  IT Education (2 years f/t)
  Maths Education (2 years f/t)
  MFL Education (2 years f/t)
  Music Education (2 years f/t)
  Science Education (2 years f/t)
  English Education (3 years f/t)
  Geography Education (3 years f/t)
  Information Technology Education (3 years f/t)

- **BA Hons Education** (p/t in-service programme, non-QTS)

- **BA / BSc Hons Design & Technology Education (Secondary)** (4 years f/t)

CERTIFICATES / DIPLOMAS

- **PGCE Primary** (2 years f/t) in the following areas:
  Business
  Design & Technology
  Information Technology
  Mathematics
  Modern Foreign Languages
  Music
  Science

- **PGCE Key Stage 2/3** (2 years f/t) in the following areas:
  Design & Technology
  Mathematics
  Science

- **PGCE Secondary** (1 year f/t) in the following areas:
  Business Education
  Design & Technology
  English
  Geography
  Information Technology
  Mathematics
  Modern Foreign Language
  Music
  Science

- **Certificate in Education** (2 years p/t)

MASTER'S DEGREES

- **MA Education in**
  Children's Literature
  Design & Technology
  Music Education
  Post-16 & Community Education
  Special Educational Needs
  Teaching & Learning with ICT
  Training & Development
  Length of course: 1 year f/t, 2-3 years p/t

RESEARCH DEGREES

- **MPhil, PhD**

APPLICATIONS

Full-time undergraduate programmes: UCAS *(see Glossary)*
Postgraduate Certificate in Education: GTTR *(see Glossary)*
Other programmes: School of Education *(see contact details above)*

School of Educational Studies
GUILDFORD   GU2 7XH

T: 01483 686190
F: 01483 686191
E: e.oliver@surrey.ac.uk
W: www.surrey.ac.uk/Education

Head of School: Professor Stephen McNair

CERTIFICATES / DIPLOMAS / MASTER'S DEGREES

■ **PGCert / PGDip / MSc in Applied Professional Studies**
The following three pathways are offered:
• Education & Training
• Lifelong Learning
• Educational Technology
This modular course offers maximum flexibility through mixed mode delivery, the majority being directed self-study (distance mode).
Length of course: 3 years p/t; 1 year f/t (not every year)
Start dates are quarterly for distance mode or September for full-time mode.
Entry requirements: Approved degree or equivalent professional qualifications; relevant experience. Exemption from not more than one third of the course at PGDip level (max. 3 modules), for study of an appropriate nature, content and standard.
Course content: The course provides an intellectual base from which practitioners in education, training and other areas of learning can reflect upon and develop their practice, regardless of work setting or geographical location. It can be studied entirely at a distance and has exit points at PGCert stage (4 modules), at PGDip stage (8 modules) and at MSc stage (successful completion of a dissertation). Each pathway has different core modules. A Research Methods module is compulsory in all pathways.
Assessment: Essay assignments or project work; plus dissertation for the award of MSc.
Fees:
Part-time: *EU students:* £1310; *Non-EU students:* £1400 (stage fee)
Full-time: *EU students:* £3930; *Non-EU students:* £7750
Enquiries: Mrs Elizabeth Oliver *(contact details above)*

■ **PGDip/MSc Change Agent Skills & Strategies**

■ **PGDip/PGCert/MSc Counselling & Psychotherapy as a Means to Health**

■ **MSc Research Methods** *(subject to validation)*
Recognised by ESRC for part-time studentships.

RESEARCH DEGREES

- **MPhil, PhD**

The School is recognised by the ESRC on a '1+3' basis for part-time and collaborative (CASE) students.

Length of course: 5 years p/t (max)

Entry requirements: Normally a good first degree or a Master's degree; at least 3 years' professional experience.

Course content: Students are required to attend a Methods of Inquiry course in their first year. The course provides a thorough grounding in qualitative and quantitative methodologies and encourages the development of a strong research community which supports individuals throughout their studies.

Current areas of research fall broadly into the following areas:

- Professional & Work-related Learning
- Change Management & Therapeutic Education
- Lifelong & Community Learning
- Policy & Change in Higher Education
- Nursing & Midwifery Education

Institute of Education
Education Development Building
Falmer
BRIGHTON   BN1 9RG

T: 01273 678039
F: 01273 678568
E: d.usie@sussex.ac.uk
W: www.sussex.ac.uk/usie

Director: Dr Fiona Leach

The Institute of Education offers a large MA programme, an innovative school-based teacher training programme, substantial involvement in management education and many funded research projects. Graduate programmes are located within the *Graduate Research Centre in Education* which provides a stimulating and supportive environment for a wide range of research.

The Centre for International Education (Director: Professor Keith Lewin) comprises a group of faculty with extensive experience both of teaching overseas students in the UK and of overseas research and development work in education. They have particular expertise and interest in the following areas:
• Curriculum Development
• Assessment & Evaluation
• Gender
• Teacher Education
• Policy & Planning
• Management Training
• Research Methodology

CERTIFICATES / DIPLOMAS

■ **PGCE 11-18 with QTS**
■ **PGCE 14-19 and 7-14 with QTS in Maths and Science**
This programme is based in local schools and at the University.
Length of course: 1 year f/t (mid-September - end June); 2 years p/t (Music only)
Entry requirements: Relevant degree recognised as being of UK equivalence; GCSE grade C or above in English Language and Maths or equivalents.
Course content: Subjects offered:
• Citizenship with History
• English
• Geography
• History
• Maths
• MFL
• Music
• Science
Fees: EU students: £1100 f/t *(if self-financing)*
       Non-EU students: £7550 f/t
Enquiries: Admissions, Office for Initial Teacher Education *(address see above);* usie.oite@sussex.ac.uk; T: 01273 678405; F: 01273 678411

MASTER'S DEGREES

■ MA in International Education

This programme has been developed for professionals in education who wish to expand their understanding of issues relating to educational development and to acquire new skills to enhance their professional practice.

The programme examines educational issues and trends from an international perspective but focuses especially on the challenges which face resource-constrained or rapidly expanding educational systems.

By the end of the programme students will have:

• Developed their theoretical and practical understanding of key issues relating to education and development both in general terms and with respect to their chosen specialisms

• Enhanced their critical awareness of the dynamics of educational change at the local, national and/or international level

• Developed research and evaluation skills which could be applied in their future professional settings

Length of course: 1 year f/t (October to the following August); 2 years sandwich [Students spend one full term at Sussex (October to December), followed by four terms part-time study in their own country, returning for a final full term at Sussex (April to August the following year).]

New: A split-site version of the programme is offered to cohorts of students at both MA and Diploma level.

Entry requirements: Normally a good first degree and appropriate qualifications; professional experience.

Programme content: The programme consists of a core component and a choice of one of the following five specialist strands:

• Curriculum Development
• Teacher Education
• Assessment & Examination
• Primary Education
• Gender & Education

Core and specialist components run concurrently over three academic terms.

Assessment: Two 4-5,000 word essays; a 8-10,000 word research project; a 18-20,000 word major project.

Fees: 1-year f/t: *EU students: £2950; Non-EU students: £7550*
        Sandwich version: *EU students: £1440pa; Non-EU students: £3645pa*

Enquiries: Margaret Ralph; margmr@sussex.ac.uk; T: 01273 678260; F: 01273 678568; *(address see beginning of entry)*

■ MA in Education Studies

Education Studies is a new programme which offers a flexible approach to Masters level work. Although not a distance degree, the MA in Education Studies is particularly suitable for those who are unable to be at Sussex continuously. The registration periods are flexible and there is the possibility of tutorial supervision via email, fax, telephone and airmail. This allows students to conduct research in their own professional environment.

Education Studies is distinctive because students choose their own area of study within the broad discipline of education, constructing their own coherent integrated learning experience and teaching focuses on one-to-one supervision with a tutor with expertise in their area of interest. The student may choose to carry out library based work, research in the field, or enquiry at his/her own workplace. There are different patterns of assessment, so the student can select the one that best fits their needs and can pace their studies to suit individual circumstances. A diploma is also availabe (details on request).

Length of course: 1-3 years f/t; 2-5 years p/t

Entry requirements: Normally a good first degree or a first degree and relevant professional experience.

Programme content: There is no set programme of study, this being determined by students in consultation with their supervisor.

Fees: EU students: £2950
      Non-EU students: £7550

Enquiries: MA and Postgraduate Coordinator; ma-usie@sussex.ac.uk; T: 01273 678447; F: 01273 678568; (address see beginning of entry)

RESEARCH DEGREES

■ MPhil, DPhil

The Institute is keen to attract applications from experienced practitioners who wish to undertake research relating to aspects of their job and from social scientists who wish to undertake empirical research within Education. Distinctive aspects of research in the Institute of Education are its close involvement with schools and colleges and its open attitude to existing methodology and theory. We have a particularly strong track record in

- Curriculum Development
- Curriculum & Institutional Evaluation
- Gender
- Learning, Teaching & Assessment
- Maths & Science Education
- Planning & the Management of Change
- Professional & Vocational Education and Adult Education
- Science Education
- Social Inclusion
- Special Education
- Student Voice
- Studies of Educational Policy, Planning & Finance
- Teacher Education

Our research training programme is recognised by the ESRC for full-time and part-time study. We have a substantial number of students from overseas carrying out research in a wide range of contexts (see our website at www.sussex.ac.uk/usie/rd/)

Facilities for research students include computer support in a research student work base, extensive library resources, research methods seminar programmes and links between the Institute of Education and other groups within the University, particularly the Institute of Development Studies and the Graduate Research Centre in Culture,

UNIVERSITY OF SUSSEX

Development and the Environment.
A sample of current DPhil and MPhil topics and a list of doctorates awarded since 1999 are available on our website.
Length of course: MPhil: 3 terms (min) f/t; 6 terms p/t (min)
DPhil: 6 terms f/t (min); 9 terms p/t (min)
Average period of study for f/t DPhil students is 9 terms, ie 3 years.
Entry requirements: Normally a degree and an MA in Education or a related subject; applications will also be considered if applicants have qualifications and experience which are judged an appropriate preparation for the research they wish to undertake. Upgrading from MPhil to DPhil is possible, depending on progress of research.
Fees: EU students: £2950 (f/t)
        Non-EU students: £7550 (f/t)
Where students are based in a well-funded research environment overseas, it is also possible to register as a Collaborative or Independent Distance student spending substantially less time in residence at Sussex and with a reduced fee.
Enquiries: Margaret Ralph; margmr@sussex.ac.uk; T: 01273 678260; F: 01273 678568; (address see beginning of entry)

- **Professional Doctorate in Education (EdD) by distance registration**
This innovative split-site EdD programme offers study at the doctoral level in a structured way through a combination of University of Sussex and home-country based taught components followed by a research thesis. The intensive modules will be taught by Sussex academics to a cohort of students both in a local collaborating institution in their home country and at Sussex. This will mean that participants can remain in their home country for almost the whole period of their registration.
This degree will provide the opportunity for experienced professionals in educational institutions, other public service organisations, NGOs or CBOs to work at doctoral level on issues and problems that are of direct relevance to their own professional interests and institutional concerns.
Length of course: 4 years p/t
Entry requirements: as for MPhil/DPhil
Fees: negotiable depending on size of cohort and specific programme inputs
Enquiries: as for MPhil/DPhil

OTHER COURSES

- **Short Courses**
Short courses can be designed and delivered to meet the needs of specific groups of clients. Recent examples are:
- Primary Education
- Management development for senior primary educational administrators from Pakistan
- Evaluation of curriculum activities in Malaysia
- Women and educational management in Zambia
- Curriculum upgrading for secondary schools in Sri Lanka
- Curriculum development training for senior Ministry of Education officials from Kuwait
- Teacher Education Management & Leadership Development Programme for Sri Lankan College Principals
Fees: Vary according to length of course and number of participants.

Faculty of Education
Brownberrie Lane
Horsforth
LEEDS LS18 5HD

T: 0113 283 7100
F: 0113 283 7200
E: admissions@tasc.ac.uk
W: www.tasc.ac.uk

Trinity and All Saints (TAS) is a Catholic foundation and an accredited College of the University of Leeds. The Faculty of Education at TAS offers a wide range of degree and graduate diploma courses. These include:
• BA Hons in Primary Education with QTS
• Graduate Certificate in Education (Secondary) with QTS
• MPhil and PhD by research

■ Graduate Certificate in Education (Secondary) with QTS

Length of course: From mid-September to early July the following year
Entry requirements: A first degree in a subject relevant to secondary school curriculum; GCSE English Language and Maths at grade C or higher or equivalent.
Course content: The course prepares students to teach the following specialist subjects at secondary level:
• Business Studies
• Citizenship
• English
• History
• Maths
• MFL (French, German, Spanish)
• RE
The course includes a substantial amount of school-based training in partnership schools.
Fees: £5967
Enquiries: Kathryn Molloy, Admissions and Marketing

RESEARCH DEGREES

■ MPhil, PhD

Length of course: MPhil: 2 years
PhD: 3 years
Entry requirements: A first degree in the relevant subject area.
Research areas:
• Special Educational Needs
• Educational Assesment
• Ethos of a Catholic School
Fees: £6608
Enquiries: Dr Roy Todd, Director of Research

UNIVERSITY OF WALES - ABERYSTWYTH

Department of Education
Old College, King Street
ABERYSTWYTH SY23 2AX

T: 01970 622 103/7
F: 01970 622 258
E: mbb@aber.ac.uk
W: www.aber.ac.uk/education

Head of Department: Professor Paul Ghuman

BACHELOR DEGREES

■ **BA Joint Honours Education**
Length of course: 3 years
Entry requirements: A-levels or equivalent in any subject.
Course content/structure: This scheme explores ways in which children learn. It includes issues which are central to an understanding of educational systems, ie curriculum design, educational policy, as well as psychology and the study of language. The degree may be studied in combination with a wide range of subjects.
Assessment: A combination of course work and formal examination.
Fees: *EU students:* £1075; *Non-EU students:* £6830
Enquiries: Admissions Tutor *(contact details see above)*

RESEARCH DEGREES

■ **MPhil, PhD**
The Department offers supervision in a wide range of areas including:
• Bilingualism
• Education Policy in Wales
• Ethnic Minorities
• Health Education
• Language & Gender
• Language & Learning
• Literacy
• New Technology / ICT
Length of course:
MPhil: 1 year (min) f/t; 2 years (min) p/t
A candidature will lapse if a thesis is not submitted within 3 years of f/t research or within 5 years of p/t research.
PhD: Candidates with Master's degree: 2 years (min) f/t; 3 years (min) p/t
        Other candidates: 3 years (min) f/t; 5 years (min) p/t
A candidature will lapse if a thesis is not submitted within 5 years of f/t research or within 7 years of p/t research.
Entry requirements: A good honours degree; professional experience in the world of education.
Assessment: *MPhil:* dissertation of ca. 60,000 words
        PhD: dissertation of ca. 100,000 words
Students study under the supervision of a tutor.
Fees: *EU students:* £2805; *Non-EU students:* £6830
Enquiries: The Higher Degrees Secretary *(contact details see beginning of entry)*

School of Education
Normal Site, Holyhead Road
BANGOR LL57 2PX

T: 01248 382932
F: 01248 383092
E: eds056@bangor.ac.uk
W: www.bangor.ac.uk

<u>Head of School:</u> Professor Gareth Roberts

RESEARCH DEGREES

■ **MPhil, PhD**

Research degrees may be pursued in the following areas:
• Bilingualism & Bilingual Education
• Maths
• Science & Technology Education
• Welsh Medium Education

<u>Length of course:</u> *MPhil:* 2 years
                PhD: 3 years

<u>Entry requirements:</u> Degree in appropriate subject.

<u>Fees:</u> EU students: £2740
      Non-EU students: £6800

<u>Enquiries:</u> Professor Colin Baker; eds056@bangor.ac.uk; T: 01248 383000

UNIVERSITY OF WALES - SWANSEA

Department of Education
Hendrefoelan
SWANSEA SA2 7NB

T: 01792 205678 or 518682
F: 01792 298499 or 290219
E: s.e.davies@swansea.ac.uk
W: www.swan.ac.uk

Head of Department: Professor Maurice Whitehead

The Department welcomes overseas teachers, headteachers, lecturers and administrators.

CERTIFICATES / DIPLOMAS

■ **PGCE Primary and Secondary**
A professional preparatory course for those wishing to enter the primary or secondary sector.
Length of course: 1 year f/t
Entry requirements: Degree or equivalent; GCSE English, Mathematics at grade C or equivalent; for Primary also Science at grade C or equivalent.
Assessment: Written assignments; practical school experience.
Enquiries: University Admissions Office; T: 01792 295111 *(further contact details see above)*

MASTER'S DEGREES

■ **MA Education**
Length of course: 12 months (min) - 2 years (max) f/t;
              2 years (min) - 5 years (max) p/t
Entry requirements: First degree or special exemption.
Course content:
Part I:
All students follow a double module in Educational Research plus two modules chosen from:
• Curriculum & Assessment
• Educational Management
• Psychology of Learning
In addition they follow four modules in a specialised strand selected from:
• Improving Learning through Teaching
• Improving Schools
• Leading your Subject
• Special Education
• Management in Education
• Specific Learning Difficulties (Dyslexia)
• Mathematics Education
• Teacher as Researcher
Part II:
A dissertation of up to 20,000 words.

RESEARCH DEGREES

■ **MPhil, PhD**

<u>Entry requirements:</u> Degree and relevant English Language qualification.

<u>Research areas:</u>
- Teacher Education
- Educational Policy
- School Management
- History of Education
- Mathematics Education
- Teaching of individual subjects

Supervision and programmes of work can be organised to meet the needs of individuals.

<u>Enquiries:</u> Division of Graduate Studies; T: 01792 518620 *(further contact details see beginning of entry)*

In addition to courses related specifically to teacher education, the Department also offers a BSc(Econ) in Early Childhood Studies. Information about these courses may be obtained from the University Admissions Office (T: 01792 295111).

Institute of Education
Westwood
COVENTRY   CV4 7AL

T: 024 7657 2880
F: 024 7652 4177
E: wie@warwick.ac.uk
W: www.warwick.ac.uk/wie

<u>Director:</u> Professor Chris Husbands

The University of Warwick has established itself firmly within the leading group of British research universities and the most recent research assessment exercise by the Higher Education Funding Council placed it within the top five. It is committed to reinforcing its position and enhancing its existing international links.

The Institute of Education is a top-rated teaching department with the highest OFSTED-rated taught Master's courses in the United Kingdom, in the top ten nationally for initial teacher training and identified as a fast-track training department by the Department for Education and Skills. Education at Warwick was awarded 24/24 by the Quality Assurance Agency.

The Institute of Education is one of the largest providers of both initial teacher education and continuing professional development within the UK. It offers a range of higher degrees, through both taught and research programmes, in conjunction with its associated research centres and units:

* The Centre for Education & Industry
* The Mathematics Education Research Centre
* The Centre for Research in Elementary & Primary Education
* The Centre for Educational Development, Appraisal & Research (CEDAR)
* Centre for New Technologies & Research in Education
* The Teacher Development Unit
* The Warwick Religions & Education Research Unit
* Environmental Sciences Research & Education Unit
* Special Needs Research Unit

Courses of study and research relevant to the continuing professional development of teachers, lecturers, educators and administrators are also offered by the following departments and centres of the University:

* The Department of Continuing Education
* The Centre for English Language Teacher Education (CELTE)
  (see details at end of entry)

The University is situated on a green field site on the edge of both the Coventry City boundary and rural Warwickshire, with excellent access to the road, rail and air network of the UK. There is excellent provision of residential accommodation on campus. Undergraduate overseas students are guaranteed campus accommodation for at least two years and new Postgraduate students for at least one year. An increasing proportion of postgraduates are accommodated in custom-built postgraduate campus accommodation.

International students benefit from the many support services which are available. These include the International Office; the Overseas Student Advisers; the Support for English Language and Study Skills Scheme; the Senior Tutor's Office, and the Students' Union with its own Welfare Officer and its many Societies.

The excellent relationships which the Institute of Education enjoys with neighbouring schools and colleges enables visiting students to have contact with a wide range of establishments, varying from those in small villages through to large urban multi-racial community colleges.

The Institute and The Centre for English Language Teacher Education and the Department of Continuing Education attract students, teachers and educational administrators from a wide range of countries. They provide short courses and are willing to consider individual courses and in-country courses. The emphasis at all times is on providing courses of high quality.

BACHELOR DEGREES

- **BPhil Education** (distance learning)

This is a professional, post-experience course for teachers overseas and is taught mainly in the student's home country.

Length of course: 2 (min) - 5 (max) years p/t

Entry requirements: QTS (or equivalent); normally 3 years teaching experience.

Course content: Four modules, including a dissertation.

Enquiries: CPD Office; cpd@warwick.ac.uk

- **BA Hons leading to QTS**

This is a pre-service degree course for intending primary teachers with proficiency in English. It offers students the opportunity to develop academically and professionally in an integrated way.

Length of course: 4 years f/t

Entry requirements: University's general entrance requirements; medical examination.

Course content: The course prepares students for teaching in the Primary age range (5-11) specialising in English, Maths or Science.

Applications: through UCAS (see Glossary)

Enquiries: Dr George Raper; ba-qts@warwick.ac.uk

- **BA Hons Early Childhood Studies**

This is a degree course for those interested in the development of young children. It is not a teacher training course, but offers students the opportunity to study the education and childcare services which support the child and the family.

Length of course: 3 years f/t

Entry requirements: University's general entrance requirements.

Course content: Students will follow core modules which focus upon early childhood from British and international perspectives. Optional modules allow students to develop an expertise in a particular area with the possibility of progression on to courses such as a 3-8 (early years) PGCE.

Applications: through UCAS (see Glossary)

Enquiries: Liz Coates; ba-qts@warwick.ac.uk

CERTIFICATES / DIPLOMAS

- **PGCE Early Years Primary and Secondary**

Length of course: 1 year f/t

Entry requirements: Second class (joint or single) honours degree (for secondary students this should be in their proposed specialist subject).

Course content: This is a course for graduates wishing to teach in a primary (3-8 or 5-11) or secondary school. Specialist secondary subjects available are:
- Economics with Business Studies*
- English & Drama*
- History
- ICT
- Maths*
- Modern Languages (French, Spanish, German)*
- RE*
- Science*

flexible route available in these subjects

Applications: *through GTTR (see Glossary)*

Enquiries: *Secondary:* Dr Liz Bills; *Early Years/Primary:* Dr Jane Medwell; pgce@warwick.ac.uk

■ **Diploma in English Language Teaching & Administration**
This is a course for teachers of English in secondary, tertiary and adult education overseas. Many follow it as a preliminary year of study before doing an MA.

Length of course: 8 months f/t

Entry requirements: Normally a first degree or equivalent: some teaching experience.

Enquiries: Dr Julia Khan; CELTE *(see end of entry for details)*

■ **Postgraduate Certificates**
One-term courses from the MA programmes may be taken separately, leading to a Postgraduate Certificate. A Certificate in English Language Teaching and British Cultural Studies is also available.

Length of course: 1 term (10 weeks)

Entry requirements: *as for MA degrees*

Enquiries: Dr Julia Khan; CELTE *(see end of entry for details)*

MASTER'S DEGREES

■ **MSc in Science Education**
Length of course: 1 year f/t; 2 years p/t

Entry requirements: At least a second class honours degree in Science; preferably 3 years teaching experience.

Course content: Four modules, including Research Methods in Education and a dissertation on a related topic.

Enquiries: Dr Susan Barker; wie-grad@warwick.ac.uk

■ **MSc in Mathematics Education**
Length of course: 1 year f/t; 2 years p/t

Entry requirements: At least a second class honours degree in Maths; preferably 3 years teaching experience.

Course content: Four modules, including Research Methods in Education and a dissertation on a related topic.

Enquiries: Dr Eddie Gray; wie-grad@warwick.ac.uk

- **MA in Primary Education by Research** (Cyprus)

This course is based in Cyprus.

Length of course: 1 year f/t; 2 years p/t

Enquiries: Professor Jim Campbell; wie-grad@warwick.ac.uk

- **PGCert/MA in Religious Education** (distance learning)

These courses are primarily aimed at primary and secondary school teachers, but also attract others who have professional or personal interest in the issues covered.

Length of course: MA: 2 years p/t; PGCert: 1 year p/t

Entry requirements: At least a second class Honours degree including Religious Studies or Education.

Course content: The course raises the fundamental issue of how far it is possible to understand someone else's view of the world. The question is raised at a theoretical level in field studies of religions, in discussion of religious pluralism and education and of issues in the politics and practice of religious education. The University is ideally placed for fieldwork, with a rich and varied Christian presence in the area, together with communities representing all of the major world religions.

Enquiries: Professor Robert Jackson; wie-grad@warwick.ac.uk

- **MA in Drama & Theatre Education**
- **PGCert in Drama Education**

These courses provide students with a practical and theoretical base for developing a drama and theatre education curriculum and pedagogy for schools, colleges and other educational and community contexts.

Length of course: MA: 1 year f/t or 2 years p/t; PGCert: 1 year p/t

Entry requirements: A second class honours degree and teaching experience; professional experience considered.

Course content: 4 (MA) / 3 (PGCert) modules, including Research Methods, and a dissertation on a related topic.

Enquiries: Dr Jonathan Neelands, Dr Joe Winston; wie-grad@warwick.ac.uk

- **MA in Educational Studies**

This is a course for graduates in teaching, administration or other aspects of education and is intended to provide opportunities for extended academic study and professional development in education.

Length of course: 1 year f/t; 2 years p/t

Entry requirements: At least a second class honours degree; normally 3 years' teaching experience.

Enquiries: Mr Peter Lang; wie-grad@warwick.ac.uk

- **MA in Educational Management**

Length of course: 1 year f/t; 2-3 years p/t; 2-4 years by distance learning

Entry requirements: At least a second class honours degree; at least two years' relevant experience.

Enquiries: Professor Chris Husbands; wie-grad@warwick.ac.uk

RESEARCH DEGREES

■ MA, MSc, MPhil, PhD

Many research opportunities are provided by the Institute, leading to the above degrees by full-time or part-time research. Research interests include:

- The Arts & Artists in Schools
- Behavioural Problems & School Exclusions
- Child Psychology
- Children's Learning in Science
- Children's Literature
- Computer-Assisted Learning
- Early Years Education
- Environmental Studies & Ecology
- ICT
- Language & Learning
- Management in Education
- Maths Education
- Multi-cultural Studies
- Personal & Social Education
- Primary/Secondary School Curricula
- RE & Culture
- Science Education
- SEN
- Subject, Curriculum & Assessment Studies at Primary, Secondary & Tertiary Levels
- Teacher Development
- Vocational & Technical Education
- World Studies & Political Education

Enquiries: Professor David Wray; wie-grad@warwick.ac.uk

■ EdD

This programme is designed to contribute to the advanced professional and academic development of those working in education.

Length of course: 3 years f/t; 4 years p/t

Enquiries: Professor David Wray; wie-grad@warwick.ac.uk

■ PhD, MPhil, MA in CELTE

It is possible to study for these research degrees in CELTE (see end of entry for details). The range of research interests is wide and varied and applications are welcome in the following areas:

- Linguistic Studies in English and their application (including text and discourse analysis, functional grammar, corpus linguistics, lexicography)
- Teacher Education & Development
- Language Curriculum Evaluation & Testing
- Classroom Studies & Pedagogy in English Language Teaching (including the teaching of English to young learners, the development of reading and writing processes and pedagogy, classroom interaction)

- Policy & Sociocultural Issues in English Language Teaching (including language education policy, bilingualism and bilingual education, intercultural issues in the English language classroom, onomastics)

OTHER COURSES

■ Continuing Professional Development Courses
The Institute of Education provides high quality courses in:
- Leadership & Management
- ICT
- RE
- Literacy
- Science
- Numeracy

Courses include work on:
- Improving school leadership and management
- Increasing the effectiveness of special educational needs coordinators
- The use of ICT to improve children's achievements
- Effective teaching and support for early years children

A range of services and tailor-made packages are available to meet the needs of individuals, institutions and LEAs. Accreditation of Prior Learning is possible.
Enquiries: Ann Ramsden; a.s.ramsden@warwick.ac.uk

■ Preparatory Intensive Course in English
This course is for postgraduate students who need to improve their English in order to gain entry to a British university to study any subject. Assistance is given with University placement.
Length of course: 1, 2 or 3 terms of 10 weeks each
Entry requirements: First degree
Enquiries: Rod Revell, CELTE (details see below)

CELTE

Centre for English Language Teacher Education   T: 024 7652 3200
University of Warwick   F: 024 7652 4318
COVENTRY CV4 7AL   E: celte@warwick.ac.uk
                                                       W: www.warwick.ac.uk/CELTE

The Centre for English Language Teacher Education (CELTE) has been part of the University of Warwick since 1983 and has a long-established international reputation for its postgraduate courses. It offers opportunities for development of advanced professional skills together with rigorous academic standards and a strong research base.
Over the years, CELTE has attracted students from more than 100 different countries - Britain, Europe, Africa and the Arab world, South/South East/East/Central Asia, North/South/Central America - providing the experience of working and learning alongside ELT practitioners and students from across the world.

Glossary on page XI

UNIVERSITY OF THE WEST OF ENGLAND

Faculty of Education
Frenchay Campus
Coldharbour Lane
BRISTOL BS16 1QY

T: 0117 974 1251
F: 0117 344 4208
E: admissions@uwe.ac.uk
W: www.uwe.ac.uk

Dean of Faculty of Education: Professor Joan Whitehead
Pre-application enquires: education.courses@uwe.ac.uk; T: 0117 344 4267

The Faculty of Education at UWE is one of the country's leading providers for initial teacher training and continuing professional development in the country. It offers a wide range of programmes for teachers in the primary, secondary and post-16 sectors of education, leading to the awards BA Hons, Postgraduate Certificate, Postgraduate Diploma, MA and EdD. It also offers programmes in Careers Guidance and Careers Education. There are opportunities available for specialists in the areas of Special Educational Needs, Education Management, Further, Higher and Adult Education and for professionals in other fields whose work involves education and training to gain these awards with the appropriate descriptor. Students can also register for the degree of Master of Philosophy (MPhil), Doctor of Philosophy (PhD) and Doctor of Education (EdD).
The Faculty of Education occupies a new, well-resourced building on the main UWE campus at Frenchay, Bristol with access to excellent facilities, particularly the Bolland Library and 24-hour computer rooms.

BACHELOR DEGREES

- **BA/BSc Hons Initial Teacher Education (Primary)**
Length of course: 4 years f/t
Enquiries: Enquiries and Admissions Service *(contact details see above)*

- **BA Hons Education**
- **BA Hons Education (Special Educational Needs)**
- **BA Hons Education (Educational Management)**
Length of courses: 25 weeks (min) - 4 years (max) p/t
Assessment: Module assignments and extended study.
Enquiries: CPD Office *(contact details see above)*

CERTIFICATES / DIPLOMAS

- **PGCE Primary and Secondary and Post-Compulsory/Further Education**
Length of course: 1 year f/t
Enquiries: Enquiries and Admissions Service *(contact details see above)*

- **PGDip in Education (Special Educational Needs)**
- **PGDip in Education (Educational Management)**
- **PGDip in Education Guidance (Vocational/Educational)**
- **PGDip in Education (ICT in Education)**
- **PGDip in Education (Early Years)**
- **PGDip in Careers Education**
Length of courses: 25 weeks (min) - 4 years (max) p/t
Assessment: Module assignments and extended study/research study.
Enquiries: CPD Office *(contact details see above)*

Glossary on page XI

- **PGCert in Education (Special Educational Needs)**
- **PGCert in Education (Educational Management)**
- **PGCert in Education (Early Years)**
- **PGCert in Education (ICT in Education)**
- **PGCert in Education (Learning Mentoring)**
- **PGCert in Education, Further, Adult & Higher Education**
- **PGCert in Education Guidance (Vocational/Educational)**
- **PGCert in Careers Education**

Length of courses: 15 weeks (min) - 2 years (max) p/t
Assessment: Module assignments
Enquiries: CPD Office *(contact details see beginning of entry)*

MASTER'S DEGREES

- **MA Education**
- **MA Education (Special Educational Needs)**
- **MA Education (Education Management)**
- **MA Education (Early Years)**
- **MA Education (Researching Education in the Arts)**
- **MA Guidance (Vocational/Educational)**
- **MA Education (Careers Guidance)**

Length of courses: 48 weeks (min) - 5 years (max) p/t
Assessment: Module assignments and dissertation.
Enquiries: CPD Office *(contact details see beginning of entry)*

RESEARCH DEGREES

- **MPhil, PhD**

There is a strong and active research culture in the Faculty with funded projects in educational and cross-professional research. The Faculty has a number of major national research and evaluation projects in the fields of Further Education, Higher Education and Schools, and there is a programme in international research - mostly in eastern Europe. Many Faculty researchers are engaged in consultancy work and most conduct collaborative research with local schools and educational agencies.

The Faculty has a new research centre - the Centre for Research in Education and Democracy (CRED) - which provides a focus for the development of research methodology, for research training and for research conversations.

Enquiries: Research Office *(contact details see beginning of entry)*

- **EdD**

The Professional Doctorate (EdD) is designed to lead to developments in knowledge and understanding in the field of education, to effective dissemination of that knowledge and understanding and to the improvement of practice. It is suitable for educators in schools, colleges, further and higher education institutions and professional training and education contexts of many kinds.

Length of course: 4 (min) - 5 (max) years
Assessment: Course work assignments and a 30-40,000 word thesis.
Enquiries: Research Office *(contact details see beginning of entry)*

School of Education
Gorway Road
WALSALL WS1 3BD

T: 01902 321050
F: 01902 323744
E: sed-enquiries@wlv.ac.uk
W: www.wlv.ac.uk/sed

Dean of the School of Education: Sir Geoff Hampton
Enquiries: Registry - Admissions Office

The School of Education offers a wide range of programmes for the initial training of teachers and lecturers for primary, secondary and further education phases. It welcomes overseas students for both undergraduate and postgraduate programmes.
The School also offers a wide-ranging programme of in-service education and two highly successful centres:
• Midlands Leadership Centre
• Centre for International Development & Training
Through a partnership approach these centres enable the School to address the design, organisation and delivery of a range of education and training services.
The campus is situated in pleasant and spacious surroundings.

BACHELOR DEGREES

The School operates within the University's modular programme. This gives students the flexibility of studying either a specialist degree in one subject or combining subjects in a joint degree. Students may study one or more subjects on either a part-time or full-time basis. The following subjects are available:
• Conductive Education
• Early Childhood Studies
• Education Studies
• Education Studies & Education*
• Special Needs & Inclusion in Society
* International degree in partnership with Education Faculty Amsterdam

CERTIFICATES / DIPLOMAS / MASTER'S DEGREES

The School offers a wide range of taught modules focused on:
• Leadership in Education
• Education Management
• Early Childhood Studies
• Special Needs & Inclusion
• Post-compulsory Education & Training
• Teaching & Learning
• Research
• Raising Standards & Attainment
Combinations of modules can lead to the following awards:

- **PGCert / PGDip / MA in**
  Management & Leadership in Education
  Education
- **PGCert in**
  Learning & Teaching in Higher Education
  Managing for Effective Learning
  Mentoring

Programmes have been designed for teachers, managers and senior managers in schools, further education and higher education. They are also highly appropriate to the needs of inspectors, advisors, trainers and those involved in the administration of education. The flexibility and choice available offers individuals at all stages of their careers the opportunity of part-time study to gain a recognised award of the University.

MASTER'S DEGREES

- **MSc Development Training & Education**

This programme is offered by the Centre for International Training and Development on a full-time basis.

RESEARCH DEGREES

- **MPhil, PhD**

Length of courses: 3 years f/t; 5 years p/t (4 weeks per year)

Entry requirements: Open to teachers, FE lecturers, trainers, administrators and those in related professions.

Course content/structure: The programmes comprise a combination of taught sessions and personal tutorials. Clients have regular contact with their tutors (two or more according to chosen field) while undertaking research on a topic which has direct relevance to their professional context. There is a strong system of mutual support amongst professionals working towards their degrees.

Faculty of Education and Psychology   T: 01905 855000
Henwick Grove   W: www.worc.ac.uk
WORCESTER   WR2 6AJ

General enquiries: Marketing Office, Director of International Affairs; marketing@worc.ac.uk; T: 01905 855142
Course enquiries: Stephen Bigger; s.bigger@worc.ac.uk; T: 01905 855054

The Faculty of Education and Psychology has a strong commitment to the professional development of teachers and others working in education and training. It has developed areas of teaching and research expertise in relation to:
• Early Childhood
• Environmental Education
• Learning & Teaching
• Literacy & Literature
• Policy Development, Implementation & Evaluation
• Primary Language
• Psychology
• Reflective Practice
• Special Educational Needs

BACHELOR DEGREES

■ **BA Education Studies / Early Childhood Studies**
Length of course: 3 years f/t or p/t
Course structure: These courses are available either singly or in conjunction with a range of other subjects at degree level as part of the Undergraduate Modular Scheme. *Education Studies* are offered as part of the professional development programme for teachers and others involved in educational and training. *Early Childhood Studies* is offered through a two-year Higher National Diploma route followed by a further year of degree level study. A range of routes are offered, drawing on the areas of expertise noted in the introduction above.
Assessment: Varied in a modular structure with independent study.

■ **BA Education with QTS**
Length of course: 3 years
Course content: Specialist study of one subject from: Maths, English, Science, IT, Advanced Early Years.
Assessment: In relation to the national standards required for QTS.

■ **BA Education Hons** (Inservice Degree)
Length of course: No set period - achieved by completion of modules and a CATS arrangement.
Course content: Modules on Special Needs, Early Childhood, Reflective Practice, Curriculum areas.
Assessment: By modules and CATS; dissertation.
Certificates and diplomas can be awarded within the scheme as an alternative to the degree.

CERTIFICATES / DIPLOMAS

■ **PGCE Primary and Secondary with QTS**

As part of the programme of professional development these courses are based on modules offered for the MA Education and MSc Education Management *(see below)*.
Course content: *Primary subjects:* Maths, English, Science & IT, Advanced Early Years. *Secondary subjects:* Maths, English, Science, MFL, History, Geography, Music, PE, Business Studies, Economics & Technology (Food & Textiles).
Entry requirements: First degree or equivalent; specific QTS demands.
Assessment: In relation to the national standards required for QTS.

■ **Certificate/Diploma CPD**

A range of self-standing qualifications to meet local and regional demand at undergraduate and post-graduate levels.
Assessment: Varied in a modular structure.

MASTER'S DEGREES

■ **MA Education / MSc Education Management**

These modular courses are designed to enable teachers and other education professionals to enhance their practice and professional expertise in the workplace.
Length of course: 1 year f/t; 2 years p/t
Entry requirements: First degree or equivalent.
Assessment: Written assignments and a dissertation.

RESEARCH DEGREES

■ **MPhil, PhD**

Entry requirements: Appropriate first degree qualifications or equivalent.
Research areas:
• Special Educational Needs
• Early Childhood
• Primary School Language
• Literacy & Literature
• Learning & Teaching
Enquiries: Dr Jean Webb, Deputy Director of the Graduate School; j.webb@worc.ac.uk; T: 01905 855323

OTHER COURSES

Specialist courses aimed at experienced teachers and others involved in education and related professions are offered in relation to areas of expertise noted in the introduction. In addition to the standard provision, specific courses for groups from overseas can be developed in all these areas.

UNIVERSITY OF YORK

Department of Educational Studies
YORK   YO10 5DD

T: 01904 433460
F: 01904 433459
E: educ15@york.ac.uk
W: www.york.ac.uk/depts/educ

Head of Department: Dr Bob Campbell
Enquiries: Departmental Secretary *(contact details above)*

In addition to the courses below, courses are also offered at the undergraduate and Advanced Diploma levels.

MASTER'S DEGREES

■ MA in Educational Studies

Length of course: 12 months f/t
Entry requirements: A good honours degree or equivalent; those with other qualifications, such as an advanced diploma in education or equivalent, are also encouraged to apply.
Applicants need to be able to use English to a sufficiently advanced level. To assist with this, the University's Language Teaching Centre can provide short pre-sessional courses, together with continuing support.
Course content: The first term consists of two compulsory modules
• Research Methods in Education
• Theories of Learning & Development
and one of the following option modules
• Gender and Education
• Global & International Education
• International Perspectives on Language Education
• Primary Education
• Science Education
• Teaching & Learning
The Department particularly welcomes applications in these areas, but also in other areas where staff have expertise. These include:
• Education in Developing Countries
• Education & the Law
• Evaluation of Educational Innovation
• Gender Education
• Language Education
• Maths Education
• Political & Citizenship Education
In addition, there will be regular opportunities for students to share and exchange research concerns and hear members of staff and visiting speakers talk on research matters.
Assessment: Students complete two assessed essay assignments - which contribute 40% to the overall programme assessment - and a thesis of 15,000 words.
Theses are submitted by 30 September at the end of the year of registration.

- **MA in Teaching English to Young Learners** (by distance)

Length of course: 2 years p/t

Entry requirements: Good honours degree or equivalent

Course content/structure: The teaching takes place at a distance by way of eight multimedia module packs that are given to each student for self-study. The module packs have been specifically developed by the EFL Unit and contain a mixture of materials including: Module outlines, papers, study notes, video presentations, articles, professional reflection activities and assignment outlines. The module packs will be supported by books, e-mail, fax, mailed tutorials and seminars.

Each module lasts approximately three months, allowing for study, reflection, research and writing time and postage. Within each module students can focus on 6-11 year-olds, 11-16 year-olds or 6-16 year-olds. All eight modules have a mixture of theory and practice, which can be applied directly to TEYL. The final module, the action research module, also has a summarising and review function, being designed for students to apply a variety of skills and expertise gained throughout the programme. Each year there is an obligatory two-week intensive course held at York in July to prepare for the following year's study. (Large student groups in specific countries may have the two-week intensive programmes in-county at other times of the year by prior arrangement with the EFL Unit).

Each student is assigned a supervisor who will keep in regular contact with them throughout the programme by way of e-mail, mail, fax and phone. Students will also meet with their supervisor during the two-week intensive periods in York.

Assessment: This is by way of four marked assignments in the first year, three marked assignments in the second year and a marked Action Research Project. Assignments 1, 2, 3, 5, 6 & 7 will be approximately 3,500 to 4,000 words in length. Assignments 4 & 8 are slightly different in nature, in that they will represent the cumulative and summative assessment for the relevant block of four modules in each year of study and because of this they will be up to 5,000 words in length.

Enquiries and applications: The MA Secretary, EFL Unit, Language Teaching Centre, Department of Educational Studies; efl2@york.ac.uk

RESEARCH DEGREES

- **MPhil, PhD**

Length of course: MPhil: 2 years f/t; PhD: 3 years f/t

Entry requirements: Good honours degree or a master's degree

Course content: Applications are especially welcomed from students wishing to work in one of the four areas of research where we have particular strengths:

- Humanities Education (includes English Education, Citizenship Education, International Education)
- Primary & Early Years Education
- Science Education
- Research on Teachers & Teaching

A full list of staff and their research interests can be found on our website.

FEES: *To be found at www.york.ac.uk/admin/gso/gsp/finance/fees*

SUBJECT AREA INDEX

Acronyms and abbreviations used in the index: Page

Administration / Management / Organisation / Planning, Educational

Bachelor Degrees .... Bham, Brighton, Brookes, Cardiff, CCCUC, Dur, Newc, Nottm, Ports, SHU, TAS, UNN, UWE, WalesA, Worc

Certificates/Diplomas .... APU, Bath, Bham, Brighton, Brookes, Brunel, CCCUC, Dur, Edinb, Glasg, Keele, Leicester, Linc, LJMU, Man, Mdx, Newc, Newp, Nottm, Ports, QUB, Sheff, SHU, Soton, UniS, UNN, UWE, Warwick, Wolv, Worc

Master's Degrees .... APU, Bath, Bham, Bolton, Brighton, Bristol, Brookes, Brunel, Cardiff, CCCUC, Chester, Dur, Edinb, Glam, Glasg, Glos, Hull, IoE, Keele, King's, Leeds, Leicester, Linc, Liv, LJMU, Man, MMU, Newc, Newp, Nottm, OU, Ports, QUB, Reading, Sheff, SBU, SHU Soton, TAS, UCE, UEA, UniS, UNL, UNN, UWE, WalesS, Warwick, Wolv, Worc

Research Degrees .... APU, Bath, Bham, Bolton, Brighton, Bristol, Brookes, Brunel, Cardiff, CCCUC, Chester, Dur, Edinb, Exeter, Glam, Glasg, Hull, IoE, Keele, King's, Lanc, Leeds, Leicester, Linc, Liv, LJMU, Man, Newc, Nottm, Ports, QUB, Reading, SBU, SHU, Soton, Sussex, TAS, UCE, UEA, UniS, UNN, Roehampton, UWE, WalesA, WalesS, Warwick, Wolv, Worc

Other Courses .... Brighton, IoE, Keele, Leeds, Man, MMU, SBU, UNN, Warwick, Worc

Adult, Continuing, Further & Higher Education

Bachelor Degrees .... APU, Bolton, Brookes, CCCUC, Hudd, Mdx, Plymouth, Reading, Soton, Stran, UNN, UWE, Wolv

Certificates/Diplomas .... APU, Bath, Bolton, Brighton, Brookes, Glasg, Greenw, IoE, KAC, LJMU, Mdx, Newp, Nottm, Plymouth, Reading, Sheff, SHU, Sunderl, UCE, UEL, UniS, UNN, UWE, Warwick, Wolv

Master's Degrees .... APU, Bath, Bolton, Brookes, CCCUC, Chester, DMU, Glasg, Hudd, Hull, IoE, KAC, Leeds, Liv, LJMU, Mdx, Newp, Nottm, OU, Oxford, Plymouth, Reading, Sheff, SHU, Stran, Sunderl, UCE, UEA, UEL, UniS, WalesB, Warwick, Wolv

Research Degrees .... APU, Bath, Bolton, Brookes, Brunel, Cardiff, Chester, Edinb, Exeter, Glam, Glasg, Greenw, Hull, IoE, KAC, Lanc, Liv, Mdx, Nottm, Oxford, Plymouth, Reading, Sheff, SHU, Soton, Sunderl, Sussex, UEA, UniS, Warwick, Wolv

Other Courses .... IoE, Warwick

Master's Degrees .... APU, Bath, BGC, Bham, Bolton, Brighton,
Brookes, Brunel, CCCUC, Chester, DMU, Dur,
Edinb, Glasg, Glos, Gold, Greenw, Herts,
Hudd, Hull, IoE, Keele, KAC, Lanc, Leeds,
Leicester, Linc, Liv, LJMU, Man, Mdx, MMU,
Newp, Nottm, NTU, OU, Plymouth, QUB,
Reading, Roehampton, SBU, Sheff, SHU,
Soton, Sunderl, UEA, UEL, UniS, UNN, UWE,
WalesS, Warwick, Worc, Wolv, York

Research Degrees .... APU, Bath, Bham, Brighton, Brookes, Brunel,
Cam, Cardiff, DMU, Exeter, Glasg, Glos,
Greenw, Hull, KAC, Leicester, Linc, Liv, LJMU,
Man, Nottm, Reading, SHU, Sussex, UEA,
UEL, UniS, Warwick, York

Other Courses .... Brighton, Gold, IoE, Keele, Leeds, UCLAN,
UNN, Warwick

Counselling and Guidance

Bachelor Degrees .... Newc, Roehampton, StMart

Certificates/Diplomas .... Brunel, Cam, Dur, Edinb, Glasg, LJMU, Man,
Newc, Nottm, UEA, UniS, UWE

Master's Degrees .... Brookes, Bristol, Brunel, Cam, Dur, Edinb,
Hull, LJMU, Man, Newc, Nottm, OU, Reading,
UEA, UniS, UWE, WalesB

Research Degrees .... Bristol, Brunel, Dur, Hull, IoE, Man, UEA, UniS

Other Courses .... IoE

Curriculum

Bachelor Degrees .... Brookes, Gold, Hudd, IoE, Newc, WalesA,
Worc

Certificates/Diplomas .... Bath, Cam, Gold, IoE, KAC, Leicester, Nottm,
Sheff, Soton, TAS, UniS, Worc

Master's Degrees .... APU, Bath, Brookes, Cam, DMU, Glasg, Gold,
Greenw, Herts, Hudd, Hull, IoE, KAC, Leeds,
Leicester, MMU, Newc, Nottm, OU, SBU,
Sheff, SHU, Soton, Sussex, UCLAN, UEA,
UniS, UNL, UNN, WalesS, Warwick, Worc,
York

Research Degrees .... APU, Bath, Brookes, Brunel, Cam, Exeter,
Glasg, Gold, Greenw, Herts, Hudd, Hull, IoE,
KAC, Lanc, Leeds, Leicester, Man, MMU,
Nottm, SBU, SHU, Soton, Sussex, UEA, UniS,
UNL, WalesA, Worc, York

Other Courses .... Brighton, Cam, IoE, Leeds, MMU, SBU,
UCLAN, UNN, Worc

Design
see also Arts Education, Technology

Bachelor Degrees .... BGC, Greenw, LJMU, Mdx, NTU

Certificates/Diplomas .... LJMU, NTU, UEL

Master's Degrees .... LJMU

Research Degrees ....

Other Courses .... Mdx

Leisure Studies
see Physical Education / Sport, Health and Leisure Studies
Linguistics
see Language Studies / Linguistics
Management
see Administration / Management / Organisation / Planning, Educational
Mathematical Education

Bachelor Degrees .... BGC, Brighton, Cam, Chester, Gold, Greenw, LJMU, MMU, Newp, Plymouth, Sunderl, Warwick, Wolv

Certificates/Diplomas .... Brighton, Brookes, Brunel, Cam, Gold, IoE, KAC, Mdx, NTU, Plymouth, Soton, Sunderl, Sussex, UEA, UEL, Warwick

Master's Degrees .... Bristol, Cam, Chester, Edinb, IoE, King's, Leeds, MMU, OU, Plymouth, SBU, SHU, Soton, UEA, UEL, UNL, Warwick

Research Degrees .... Bath, Bristol, Brookes, Exeter, IoE, KAC, King's, Leeds, Man, MMU, Plymouth, Roehampton, SBU, Soton, Sussex, UEA, WalesB, Warwick

Other Courses .... Cam, IoE, MMU, SBU, UNN

Modern Languages

Bachelor Degrees .... APU, Bham, Brighton, Chester, Leeds, LJMU, Roehampton, Sunderl

Certificates/Diplomas .... APU, Bath, Bham, Brighton, Brunel, Gold, IoE, LJMU, Mdx, QUB, Reading, Soton, Sunderl, Sussex, UEA, UEL, Warwick, Wolv, Worc

Master's Degrees .... Bath, Bham, Brunel, Cam, King's, QUB, Roehampton, Soton, Worc

Research Degrees .... Bath, Bham, Exeter, IoE, King's, Man, QUB, Reading, Roehampton, Soton, UEA

Other Courses .... Brighton, IoE, Roehampton, UEA, Worc

Multicultural Education

Bachelor Degrees .... WalesA
Certificates/Diplomas .... Bath, Sheff, Soton
Master's Degrees .... Bath, Gold, IoE, Sheff, Soton, UCE
Research Degrees .... Bath, IoE, Keele, King's, Man, WalesA, York
Other Courses .... IoE

Music Education

Bachelor Degrees .... BGC, Plymouth, Reading, Roehampton, Sunderl, UCE

Certificates/Diplomas .... Exeter, Gold, IoE, Mdx, Plymouth, Soton, Sunderl, Sussex, UCE

Master's Degrees .... Exeter, IoE, Plymouth, Reading, Soton, UCE

Research Degrees .... Brookes, Exeter, IoE, Reading, Roehampton, Soton, UCE, UEA

Other Courses .... IoE, UEA

Nursery Education
see Primary and Nursery Education

Urban Education
Bachelor Degrees ....
Certificates/Diplomas .... Nottm, Sheff
Master's Degrees .... King's, Nottm, Sheff
Research Degrees .... Keele, King's, Stirl
Other Courses ....

Vocational Education
Bachelor Degrees .... Bolton, Cardiff, Hudd, UNN, Wolv
Certificates/Diplomas .... Bolton, Hudd, Soton, UNN, Wolv
Master's Degrees .... Bolton, Hudd, IoE, King's, Nottm, Soton, UCE,
UniS, Warwick
Research Degrees .... Bath, Bolton, Cardiff, Greenw, Hudd, Hull,
IoE, King's, Lanc, Man, Nottm, Soton, Sussex,
UCE, UEA, Warwick
Other Courses .... Bolton, Greenw, Hudd, Hull, IoE, UEA, UniS,
UNN

Women's Studies
Bachelor Degrees ....
Certificates/Diplomas ....
Master's Degrees .... Gold, Lanc, Nottm, Roehampton
Research Degrees .... Brunel, Gold, IoE, Keele, Lanc, Nottm, Stirl
Other Courses .... Gold, IoE

Youth and Community Studies
Bachelor Degrees .... Bham, Greenw, LJMU, UEL
Certificates/Diplomas .... Brighton, Greenw, UEL
Master's Degrees .... Bham, Brunel, King's, Sunderl, UEL, UniS
Research Degrees .... Brunel, Greenw, Reading, UEL
Other Courses ....